174 0

Handbook on the Common
Marine Isopod Crustacea of Georgia

Handbook
on the
Common Marine
Isopod Crustacea
of Georgia

By
ROBERT J. MENZIES
and
DIRK FRANKENBERG

UNIVERSITY OF GEORGIA PRESS
ATHENS

Contents

Plates and Figures

Preface

THE aim of this work is to provide senior students of marine biology and other investigators with a reasonably complete view of some of the common marine isopods off the coast of Georgia. Anatomical studies and an illustrated key to the species are presented because this type of information is not readily available in the current isopod literature, except for a key to the marine isopods of the Central California coast (Menzies and Miller, 1954). The key which Menzies and Miller present does not apply to the Eastern fauna since few, if any, species are common to both coasts; however, for lack of a more appropriate key, the Menzies and Miller key is in common use on the East Coast. This study presents a new key together with illustrations and a diagnosis of each species and references to the most pertinent literature. Information concerning the distribution of each species is also included.

The material on which this study is based came from collections made over a period of years at the Sapelo Island Research Foundation, Sapelo Island, Georgia. These collections were painstakingly sorted and cared for by Mr. Milton Gray, and his helpful efforts are a prime factor in making this study possible. Because this book is based upon collections made over several years we believe they are representative of the common species to be encountered on the shelf and bays off Georgia. In addition, Mr. Gray kindly provided detailed station data for each species and a map of the stations.

Additional collections were gathered by the junior author and by other staff, students, and visitors at the Sapelo Island Research Laboratory. These added specimens were provided by Dr. E. L. Bousfield, Dr. W. D. Burbanck, Dr. D. G. Darby, Mr. G. Davis, Mr. R. Heard, Dr. J. H. Hoyt, Mr. T. L. Linton, Mr. Fred McMurray, and Dr. O. H. Pilkey.

Space and facilities for the study were generously provided by the Sapelo Island Research Foundation, at the invitation of Dr. George H. Lauff, and by the Duke University Marine Laboratory. Secretarial and artist assistance were provided by both laboratories. The assistance of the Sapelo Island Research Laboratory artist Steven C. Sumner in the ink-in of some of the illustrations was most useful and helpful. A National Science Foundation Grant (GB-873) aided in the preparation of this work.

The assistance of Mrs. Susan Frankenberg in checking the illustrations and the keys is sincerely appreciated. Mrs. Lucille Menzies aided with the compilation of the bibliography.

Holotypes of newly described species have been deposited in the collections of the United States National Museum, Washington.

ROBERT J. MENZIES
Duke University Marine
Laboratory
Durham, North Carolina

DIRK FRANKENBERG
University of Georgia
Marine Institute
Sapelo Island, Georgia

Introduction

THE material examined in this study was collected from various habitats near Sapelo Island, Georgia, using methods best suited to the habitats. All specimens were collected from the littoral and sublittoral zones. Some were associated with biota such as sponges, shrimp, and fish. The intertidal specimens were collected either directly from pilings and beach drift or by sieving the sediments of beaches and mud flats. The specimens from the sublittoral zone were collected from the University of Georgia's research vessel, using several types of collecting gear. This gear included four types of dredges and a forty-foot otter trawl. The dredges were fabricated locally and consisted of a tumbler dredge, an oyster dredge, a modified Forster anchor dredge, and a bucket dredge similar to one designed by Dr. E. Lowe Pierce.

The specimens were either preserved directly in 70% ethyl alcohol or transferred to alcohol after initial preservation in 5% neutral formalin in sea water.

The preserved specimens were sorted into species, and typical individuals were illustrated. In most cases, the illustrations were made with a Leitz microprojection unit, although a few were made using a Wild stereomicroscope with a camera lucida attachment. The accuracy of each drawing was checked at a magnification greater than that of the original illustration. In some cases, oil immersion lenses were used to clarify difficult relationships. In most specimens the peraeopods were displaced or lost during mounting, and therefore those illustrated on our drawings of whole animals do not necessarily represent the *in vivo* position of these appendages.

ANATOMY AND RELATIONSHIPS

The anatomy of an isopod crustacean is illustrated in Plate I. The body is divisible into three major regions. From front to rear these are:

[1]

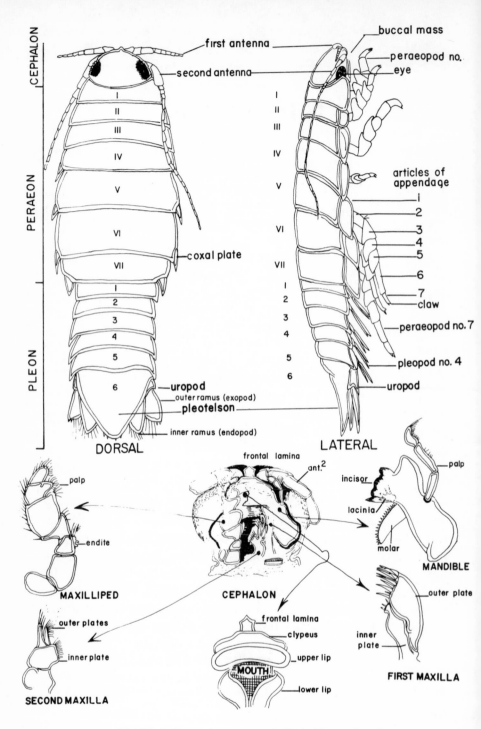

PLATE I. External anatomy of Cirolanid-type isopod

[2]

Cephalon: The most anterior region of the body bearing sessile eyes, antennae, mouth-parts, mouth, stomach, and cephalic ganglia. The cephalon is usually globular in shape.

Peraeon: The middle elongate unit of seven segments bearing paired legs, or peraeopods, intestine, gonads, and chain-like thoracic ganglia.

Pleon: The posterior unit of six ring-like segments (pleonites), each bearing paired appendages, the pleopods (five pairs), and the uropods (one pair). The anus, terminal parts of the intestine, the heart, and six pairs of nearly fused abdominal ganglia also occur in the pleon. In some isopods all somites of the pleon may be fused into a single somite. A telson is fused with the sixth pleonite to form a pleotelson.

An isopod may be distinguished from other peracaridean crustaceans by its sessile eyes, dorsoventrally compressed body, uniramous thoracic appendages, abdominal heart, five pairs of leaf-like pleopods, single pair of uropods, and seven usually distinct peraeonal somites with subsimilar, nonchelate peraeopods.

To belong to the order Isopoda an animal should have the above mentioned characteristics. Formerly (Richardson, 1905) the Chelifera (*auct.* Tanaidacea) were included in the Isopoda. They do not belong in this order because the eyes are on distinct processes; the first two peraeonal somites are fused with the head forming a carapace, thereby leaving only six free peraeonal somites; and the heart is located in the peraeon rather than in the pleon. In addition there are several more subtle differences which have been cited by Menzies (1953) and others.

The Isopoda may be divided into seven reasonably distinct groups. These are:

GROUP	TYPICAL EXAMPLE
1. Gnathiidea	*Gnathia*
2. Asellota	*Asellus*
3. Valvifera	*Idotea*
4. Flabellifera	*Cirolana*
5. Epicaridea (Bopyroidea)	*Bopyrus*
6. Oniscoidea	*Oniscus*
7. Phreatoicidea	*Phreatoicus*

It is impossible to find a single species which illustrates all the characteristics of the order Isopoda. The problems involved in selecting a typical isopod are summarized below.

The gnathiid isopods are atypical because the adults bear only five pairs of peraeopods rather than the usual seven pairs.

The asellid isopods are atypical because of their small to minute size, highly modified male pleopods, and reduced number of pleonal somites (four rather than the usual six).

The valviferan isopods are atypical because the uropods are usually inflexed under the pleon, the number of pleonal somites is reduced, and the mandibular palp is usually lacking.

The epicaridean isopods are entirely parasitic on other Crustacea, and are highly modified for this mode of existence.

The oniscoidean isopods are atypical because of their reduced antennae, generally modified pleopods, and lack of mandibular palps.

The phreatoicidean isopods are atypical because their body is laterally compressed and their uropods modified.

The flabelliferan isopods present the most nearly typical picture, but there is considerable morphological diversity even within this group. As a result of this diversity three major subgroups have been recognized within the Flabellifera. These groups are: the Anthuroidea, the Seroloidea, and the Cirolanoidea (Menzies, 1962b). The Anthuroidea are atypical because their body is long and tubular and their mouthparts are modified. The Seroloidea are atypical because the first peraeonal somite is fused to the cephalon, the seventh peraeonal somite may be absent in dorsal view, and the pleopods are modified. The Cirolanoidea include some families which are atypical, for instance in the Sphearomidae the pleon consists of only four segments rather than the usual six. But despite these difficulties we have selected the cirolanoid genus *Cirolana* (Cirolanidae) for illustration (Plate 1) as a more or less typical isopod since it shows a high percentage of primitive features. In this genus, however, the mandibles depart from the basic isopod pattern since the molar process has a sharp-toothed, knife-like edge rather than the primitive grinding type which prevails among the majority of isopods.

PREVIOUS WORK

Literature on the isopods of the Atlantic coast is recorded in Richardson's (1905) monograph. Since this monograph there

[4]

have been a few papers by Pearse and his associates (Pearse and Walker, 1939) on parasitic species, the monograph by Menzies (1962a) on the abyssal species, and a few other isolated taxonomic or ecologic papers. But in general very little work has been done on the Atlantic coastal isopods since Richardson's publication.

The need for systematic studies on the local fauna is recognized by most marine laboratories but few have made any serious attempts to provide up-to-date illustrated studies of their fauna. Such studies are rather urgently needed to provide students and scholars with a reasonably accurate picture of the wealth of species available in a local fauna for other biological work. Without such basic references the scientist is led to believe that the systematic knowledge is complete and is represented in the older works. This is emphatically not the case. This study yielded ten species and one genus of isopods which are new to science. This number of new forms accounts for 33 per cent of the total isopod fauna which was studied in this report.

However, it must be emphasized that this work is not complete. This is illustrated by the fact that Richardson (1905) recorded 106 species which had been known between Chesapeake Bay and the Caribbean. Only 12 of these are found in this study; yet all might be expected to occur off Georgia.

Table I presents a list of the species which might be found off Georgia. Those encountered in the work reported here are shown in bold-face type; parasitic forms are marked with an asterisk.

Table 1

ISOPOD SPECIES WHICH MIGHT BE FOUND OFF SAPELO ISLAND, GEORGIA (from Richardson, 1905).

No. Species	Location
1. *Aega antillensis**	Cuba, West Indies, off Cozumel
2. *Aega dentata**	Cuba
3. *Aega ecarinata**	Little Bahama Bank; between Mississippi delta and Cedar Keys, Fla.; entrance to San Juan

No.	Species	Location
4.	*Aega gracilipes**	Gulf of Mexico; North Atlantic, Latitude 59° N, Longitude 8.5° W.
5.	*Aega incisa**	Off Fernandina, Fla.; off Georgia; off St. Augustine, Fla.
6.	*Aega tenuipes**	Cuba
7.	*Aega webbii**	Off Fernandina, Fla.; Cape of Good Hope; Portugal
8.	*Aegathoa linguifrons**	Trinidad
9.	*Aegathoa medialis**	Chesapeake Bay
10.	**Aegathoa oculata**	Savin Rock, near New Haven, Conn.; Ft. Macon, N. C.; St. Thomas, West Indies. Parasite of squid (*Loligo pealii*); young mullet.
11.	*Agarna carinata**	St. Croix, West Indies; Key West, Fla. On *Teuthis chirurgus*
12.	*Alcirona hirsuta**	St. Thomas, West Indies
13.	*Alcirona krebsii**	West Indies; Bermudas. In bathing sponges; on Hamlet Grouper
14.	*Anilocra laticauda**	Maryland to Straits of Magellan On *Haemulon plumieri* and *Upeneus martinicus*
15.	*Anthelura affinis*	Bermudas
16.	*Arcturus caribbaeus*	Caribbean Sea
17.	*Bopyrina abbreviata**	Off Puntarasa, Fla. on *Hippolyte zostericola*
18.	*Bopyrina thorii**	Key West, Fla. on *Thor floridanus*
19.	*Bopyrina urocaridis**	Puntarasa, Fla. and West Fla., on *Urocaris longicaudata*
20.	**Branchuropus littoralis**	Puerto Rico
21.	*Calathura crenulata* (*Acalathura crenulata*)	Bahamas, Yucatan
22.	*Carpias bermudensis*	Bermuda
23.	*Ceratothoa impressa**	Gulf Stream; Cape May, N. J.; Rio de Janeiro, Brazil

[6]

No.	Species	Location
24.	**Chiridotea caeca**	Florida; Halifax, Nova Scotia; New England coast
25.	*Cilicaea carinata*	Coast of Georgia
26.	**Cilicaea caudata**	Egg Harbor, N. J.; Beaufort, N. C.; Florida; Yucatan; Bermudas; Bahamas
27.	*Cilicaea linguicauda*	Yucatan
28.	*Cirolana albida*	Sugar Loaf Key, Fla.
29.	*Cirolana borealis*	Off Cape Florida, Atlantic coast of North America
30.	*Cirolana concharum*	Nova Scotia to South Carolina
31.	*Cirolana gracilis*	St. Thomas, West Indies
32.	*Cirolana impressa*	Chesapeake Bay; off Cape Hatteras
33.	*Cirolana mayana*	Coast of Yucatan; Puerto Rico; San Francisco Bay, Calif.
34.	*Cirolana minuta*	St. Thomas, West Indies
35.	*Cirolana obtruncata*	Jamaica, Puerto Rico
36.	**Cirolana parva**	Key West, Fla.; Bahamas; Gulf of Mexico; West Indies
37.	*Cirolana sphaeromiformis*	St. Thomas, West Indies
38.	**Cleantis planicauda**	Florida; Puerto Rico
39.	*Colanthura tenuis*	Bermudas
40.	*Colopisthus parvus*	Bermudas
41.	*Conilera cylindracea**	South Carolina; Gulf of Mexico; Coast of England
42.	**Cyathura carinata (polita)**	Atlantic and Gulf Coast
43.	*Cymothoa caraibica**	Haiti
44.	**Cymothoa excisa**	Mass.-Fla. reefs; Biloxi, Miss.; Cuba; Rio de Janerio, Brazil
45.	*Cymothoa oestrum**	Caribbean Sea and Gulf of Mexico to Virginia. Parasite on a number of species of fishes.
46.	*Dynamene angulata*	No name Key, Fla.
47.	*Dynamene moorei*	Puerto Rico; Bermudas; on mangrove roots

[7]

No.	Species	Location
48.	*Dynamene perforata*	Puerto Rico; Bermudas; on mangrove roots
49.	**Erichsonella filiformis**	Florida; New England; Bahamas
50.	*Erichsonella floridana*	Key West, Fla.
51.	*Eurydice convexa*	Cape San Blas, Fla.
52.	*Eurydice spinigera*	West Indies
53.	*Exocorallana antillensis*	Key West, Fla.; West Indies
54.	*Exocorallana fissicauda*	West Indies
55.	*Exocorallana mexicana*	Gulf of Mexico
56.	*Exocorallana oculata*	West Indies
57.	*Exocorallana quadricornis*	West Indies; Bermudas
58.	*Exocorallana sexticornis*	Key West, Fla.
59.	*Exocorallana subtilis*	West Indies
60.	*Exocorallana tricornis*	Gulf of Mexico; Puerto Rico; West Indies
61.	*Exocorallana warmingii*	Yucatan
62.	*Exosphaeroma crenulatum*	Bermudas
63.	*Exosphaeroma faxoni*	Florida
64.	*Exosphaeroma yucatanum*	Yucatan
65.	*Gnathia cristata**	Lat. 72° 32′ N., Long. 58° 51′ W.
66.	*Grapsicepon edwardsii**	Florida Stream; Sargasso Sea
67.	*Idothea baltica*	Nova Scotia to N. C.; Bermuda; Barbados
68.	*Idothea metallica*	Halifax, Nova Scotia to Florida Keys
69.	*Irona nana**	Caribbean Sea, in gills of *Hemirhamphus* sp.; on *Atherina harringtonensis*, and on *Atherina* sp.
70.	*Jaeropsis rathbunae*	Bermudas
71.	*Janira minuta*	Bermudas
72.	*Ligyda baudiniana*	Miami, Fla.; Cuba; Bahamas
73.	*Ligyda exotica*	Beaufort, N. C., to Florida Keys; Gulf of Mexico; Calif.; Pantropic

[8]

No.	Species	Location
74.	Ligyda olfersii	Key West and Puntarasa, Fla.; St. Thomas; Brazil
75.	Limnoria lignorum	Florida to Nova Scotia; San Diego, Calif.
76.	Livoneca ovalis*	Massachusetts to Alabama
77.	Livoneca redmanni*	Cuba; Rio de Janeiro, Brazil
78.	Meinertia deplanata	Haiti
79.	Meinertia transversa*	Between delta of Mississippi River and Cedar Keys, Fla.
80.	Nalicora rapax*	Puerto Rico; Gulf of Mexico
81.	Nerocila acuminata*	Atlantic Ocean and Gulf of Mexico; Newport, Va.; St. Mary's River, Fla. Parasites of the sawfish
82.	Nerocila lanceolata*	Cumberland Island, Ga.
83.	**Olencira praegustator***	Lower Chesapeake Bay; St. Mary's River, Fla.; Gulf of Mexico. Parasite of Brevoortia patronus; B. tyrannus; bug-fish.
84.	Paradynamene benjamensis	"from the Gulf weed"
85.	Paranthura infundibulata	Bermudas
86.	Paranthura verrillii	Bermudas
87.	Probopyrus alphei*	Beaufort, N. C.; Destero, Brazil; on Crangon heterochaelis
88.	Probopyrus floridensis*	above St. John's River, Fla. on Palaemonetes exilipes
89.	Probopyrus latreuticola*	Beaufort, N. C.; Bahamas; Bermudas on Latreutes ensiferus
90.	Probopyrus pandalicola*	New Hampshire to Florida on Palaemonetes vulgaris
91.	Pseudione curtata*	Key West, Fla. on Petrolisthes sexspionosus
92.	Pseudione furcata*	Virginia, eastern shore
93.	Rocinela americana*	Lat. 37° 25′ N.; Long. 74° 18′ W.
94.	Rocinela cubensis*	Cuba
95.	Rocinela dumerilii*	Cuba

[9]

No.	Species	Location
96.	*Rocinela insularis**	West Indies; Gulf of Mexico; off Fernandina, Fla.
97.	*Rocinela oculata**	Lat. 32° 18′ 20″ N.; 78° 43′ W.
98.	*Rocinela signata**	West Indies; Florida keys; Gulf of Mexico
99.	**Sphaeroma destructor**	Florida
100.	**Sphaeroma quadridentatum**	New England to Key West, Fla.
101.	*Stegias clibanarii*	Bermudas on *Clibanarius tricolor*
102.	*Stenetrium antillense*	West Indies, found on corals in deep water
103.	*Stenetrium occidentale*	West Indies
104.	*Stenetrium serratum*	West Indies
105.	*Stenetrium stebbingi*	Bermudas

LIST OF SPECIES STUDIED

The thirty species encountered in this study are shown in the following list:

No. Name

1. *Astacilla* n. sp.
2. *Edotea montosa* (Stimpson)
3. *Cleantis planicauda* Benedict
4. *Erichsonella filiformis filiformis* (Say)
5. *Chiridotea caeca* (Say)
6. *Chiridotea* n. sp.
7. *Pseudione* n. sp.
8. *Aegathoa oculata* (Say)
9. *Lironeca* n. sp.
10. *Cymothoa excisa* Perty
11. *Olencira praegustator* (Latrobe)
12. *Serolis* n. sp.
13. *Ptilanthura* n. sp.
14. *Cyathura polita* (Stimpson)
15. *Cyathura burbancki* Frankenberg
16. *Accalathura* ? juvenile
17. *Xenanthura brevitelson* Barnard
18. *Pananthura* n. sp.

[10]

19. *Apanthura* n. sp.
20. Anthuridae n. gen. and n. sp.
21. *Ancinus depressus* (Say)
22. *Paracerceis caudata* (Say)
23. *Exosphaeroma* n. sp.
24. *Cassidinidea lunifrons* (Richardson)
25. *Sphaeroma quadridentatum* Say
26. *Sphaeroma destructor* (Richardson)
27. *Eurydice littoralis* Moore
28. *Eurydice* n. sp.
29. *Cirolana polita* (Stimpson)
30. *Cirolana parva* Hansen

1a. pleon of valviferan isopod, lateral view
1b. same, dorsal view
1c. dorsal view of pleon and uropods of flabelliferan isopod
2a. lateral view of arcturid isopod
3a. isopod with first through third peraeopods distinctly subchelate
3b. isopod with distinctly subchelate peraeopods
4a. second antennae four times as long as first
4b. second antennae less than twice as long as first
5a. pleon with four somites
5b. pleon with single somite
6a. lateral margin of cephalon incised
6b. lateral margin of cephalon entire
7a. pleon not immersed in peraeon
7b. pleon immersed in peraeon
8a. cephalon immersed in peraeon
8b. cephalon not immersed in peraeon
9. pleon with 3 fully separated somites
10. sixth pleonal somite fused to pleotelson mid-dorsally
11. sixth pleonal somite not fused to pleotelson mid-dorsally
12a. fourth joint of peraeopod over-riding fifth
12b. fourth joint of peraeopod not over-riding fifth
13a. mandible with uniarticulate palp
13b. mandible with multiarticulate palp
14a. palp of maxilliped with no more than five articles
14b. palp of maxilliped with more than five articles
15a. pleonal somites distinct, first pleopod larger than the others
15b. pleonal somites distinct, all pleopods subsimilar
16. uniramous uropods
17a. pleopod with both rami fleshy and provided with transverse folds
17b. pleopod with only endopod fleshy and provided with transverse folds
18. dorsum of pleon with regular transverse rows of tubercles
19a. setae on apex of pleotelson much longer than crenulations
19b. setae on apex of pleotelson scarcely longer than crenulations
20a. endopod of uropod incised on lateral border
20b. endopod of uropod not incised on lateral border

[12]

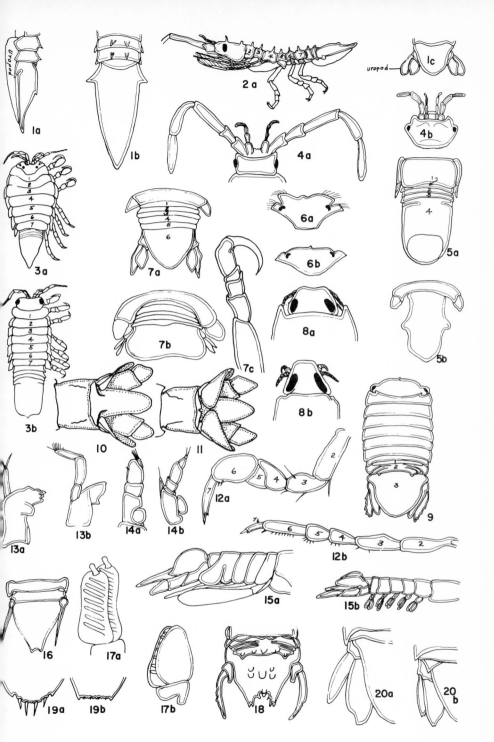

PLATE. II. Key Characteristics of Marine Isopods

[13]

A Key to the Species Treated in This Study

THIS key provides direct reference to an illustration on Plate II where the reader may see the characteristics which are described. It is our hope that the illustrations will permit the key to be used efficiently and will stimulate the reader to attempt to identify these animals for himself. The key is one of convenience; it is not meant to be a "natural key" nor to imply strict phylogenetic relationships.

1. Uropoda, large, inflexed under pleon, but not visible in dorsal view 2
   (Fig. 1a, 1b)
1. Uropoda lateral or flexed over pleon or absent 7
   (Fig. 1c)
2. First peraeonal somite fused with cephalon. Last three pairs of peraeopods somewhat claw-like. Anterior four pairs of peraeopods provided with long plumose setae, directed toward mouth and not claw-like ....
   (Fig. 2a)

   (1) *Astacilla lauffi* sp. nov.

2. First peraeonal somite not fused with cephalon. All seven pairs of peraeopods somewhat claw-like 3
   (Fig. 3a,b)

   Idoteidae

3. First three pairs of peraeopods distinctly subchelate, remainder not subchelate and do not look like the first three 6
   (Fig. 3a)

   Chirodotea

3. First leg only somewhat subchelate, all legs subsimilar 4
   (Fig. 3b)

[14]

4. Second antenna four or more times the length of first ____ 5
   (Fig. 4)
4. First antenna only slightly shorter than second antenna ____
   (Fig. 4)
                     (2) *Edotea montosa* (Stimpson)
5. Pleon with at least four somites indicated dorsally _____
   (Fig. 5a)
                     (3) *Cleantis planicauda* Benedict
5. Pleon with only a single somite indicated dorsally _____
   (Fig. 5b)
              (4) *Erichsonella filiformis filiformis* (Say)
6. Lateral margin of cephalon deeply cleft, with distinct
   preocular lobes _____
   (Fig. 6a)
                        (5) *Chiridotea caeca* (Say)
6. Lateral margin of cephalon not deeply cleft, without
   preocular lobes _____
   (Fig. 6b)
                     (6) *Chiridotea stenops* sp. nov.
7. Uropoda absent _____
                        (7) *Pseudione* (?)
7. Uropoda present _____ 8
   (Fig. 1c)
8. Body tubular, about five times as long as wide _____ 14
                                        Anthuridae
8. Body flattened, about two times as long as wide _____ 9
9. All peraeopods prehensile nearly equal in shape and size 10
   (Fig. 7c)
                                       Cymothoidae
9. Peraeopods not prehensile or of two or more different
   kinds _____ 13
   (Fig. 12a)
10. Posterior margin of pleon and uropods with fine plu-
    mose setae _____
                     (8) *Aegathoa oculata* (Say)
10. Posterior margin of pleon and uropods devoid of plu-
    mose setae _____ 11
    (Fig. 1c)

11. Pleon not deeply immersed in the 7th somite of peraeon __
    (Fig. 7a)

(9) *Lironeca reniformis* sp. nov.

11. Pleon deeply immersed in seventh somite of peraeon ____ 12
    (Fig. 7b)

12. Cephalon posterior margin deeply immersed in first
    peraeonal somite _____
    (Fig. 8a)

(10) *Cymothoa excisa* Perty

12. Cephalon not deeply immersed in first peraeonal somite __
    (Fig. 8b)

(11) *Olencira praegustator* (Latrobe)

13. Four to six completely separated pleonal somites dis-
    tinct in dorsal view _____ 14
    (Fig. 5a)

13. Three or less completely separated pleonal somites
    evident in dorsal view _____ 22
    (Fig. 9)

Sphaeromidae

14. Pleopoda of two distinct and dissimilar types; first two
    pairs small and subsimilar; third pair operculiform
    and covering remaining large pleopods _____
    (Fig. 5a)

(12) *Serolis mgrayi* sp. nov.

14. All pleopoda subsimilar _____ 27

Cirolanidae

15. Fourth joint of peraeopods four through seven over-
    riding fifth _____ 17
    (Fig. 12a)

15. Fourth joint of peraeopods four through seven not
    over-riding fifth _____ 16
    (Fig. 12b)

16. Pleonal somites indistinct, all thoracic somites sub-
    equal in length _____
    (13) *Ptilanthura tricarina* sp. nov.

16. Pleonal somites distinct, last peraeonal somite one
    quarter the length of sixth, six pairs of peraeopods _____
    (16) *Accalathura* juv.

[16]

17. Palp of mandible uniarticulate or absent _____ (Fig. 13a)

          (17) *Xenanthura brevitelson* Barnard

17. Palp of mandible multiarticulate _____ 18 (Fig. 13b)

18. Maxilliped with no more than five articles _____ 19 (Fig. 14a)

18. Maxilliped with more than five articles _____ (Fig. 14b)

          (18) *Panathura formosa* sp. nov.

19. Pleonal somites one through five distinct _____ 20 (Figs. 15a, b)

19. Pleonal somites one through five indistinct _____ 21 (Figs. 10, 11)

20. Eyes present, first pleopod larger than the others, operculate, but not indurated _____ (Fig. 15a)

          (19) *Apanthura magnifica* sp. nov.

20. Eyes absent, all pleopods subsimilar, none markedly larger than others, and none operculate _____ (Fig. 15b)

          (20) *Horoloanthura irpex* gen. et sp. nov.

21. Sixth pleonal somite fused to pleotelson mid-dorsally, exopods of uropods narrow, widely separated dorsally __ (Fig. 10)

          (14) *Cyathura polita* (Stimpson)

21. Sixth pleonal somite not fused to pleotelson, incised mid-dorsally; exopods of uropods broad, may meet or overlap dorsally _____ (Fig. 11)

          (15) *Cyathura burbancki* Frankenberg

22. Uropods uniramous, consisting of a single, pointed and elongate article _____ (Fig. 16)

          (21) *Ancinus depressus* (Say)

22. Uropods biramous _____ 23 (Fig. 1c)

23. Both rami of last two pairs of pleopods fleshy and provided with transverse folds _____ 26 (Fig. 17a)

[17]

23. One or both rami of last two pairs of pleopods lack transverse folds _____ 24

24. Apex of pleon deeply incised or slightly emarginate and grooved ventrally _____ (Fig. 18)

(22) *Paracerceis caudata* (Say)

24. Apex of pleon evenly rounded _____ 25 (Fig. 9)

25. Endopod of pleopods four and five with transverse folds _____ (Fig. 17b)

(23) *Exosphaeroma diminutum* sp. nov.

25. Neither ramus of pleopods four and five with transverse folds _____

(24) *Cassidinidea lunifrons* (Richardson)

26. Dorsum of pleon smooth, without bumps or sculpture ____ (Fig. 9)

(25) *Sphaeroma quadridentatum* Say

26. Dorsum of pleon with regular transverse rows of tubercles and bumps _____ (Fig. 18)

(26) *Sphaeroma destructor* Richardson

27. Both rami of uropods look like pleopods provided with plumose setae and thin and transparent _____ 28

27. Rami of uropods longer than wide and unlike the pleopods are calcified and thickened _____ 29

28. Stout setae on apex of pleon much longer than crenulations. Color usually uniformly purple or brown _____ (Fig. 19a)

(27) *Eurydice littoralis* (Moore)

28. Stout setae on apex of pleon scarcely longer than crenulations. Color white to yellow with a few black chromatrophores _____ (Fig. 19b)

(28) *Eurydice piperata* sp. nov.

29. Endopod of uropod incised on lateral border _____ (Fig. 20a)

(29) *Cirolana polita* (Stimpson)

29. Endopod of uropod entire on lateral margin _____ (Fig. 20b)

(30) *Cirolana parva* (Hansen)

[18]

Systematic Treatment

In the systematics of the various species the simplest diagnosis possible, without duplication of generic features, has been given. Because of this the diagnoses may seem extraordinarily short. To compensate for what might appear to be omissions we have included a considerable number of descriptive illustrations which are not further described textually since they are self-explanatory. As an added complement to the species diagnoses, brief generic and familial diagnoses are included as well. The total of these diagnoses and illustrations presents a reasonably complete picture of the species involved.

There has been no attempt made to compile complete synonomies nor to seek out all the phylogenetic affinities of each species. Instead the reader is provided with a reference to the most recent work on a given taxon. This means that many subtle systematic problems remain to be resolved, and many of these have been noted.

Additionally, no effort has been made to provide a meticulous critique of the errors and omissions of the work of our predecessors since in most instances such critiques would be fruitless. For example, detailed analyses of the discrepancies between the illustrations of the species given by Stimpson (1854), Harger (1879), Richardson (1905) or Barnard (1914) would involve interpretations resulting from the poor optical equipment at their disposal and differences in interpreting the optical image at differing magnifications or resolution.

FAMILY: ARCTURIDAE
(syn. ASTACILLIDAE - Stebbing, 1905)

Reference: Nordenstam, 1933, p. 115.
Diagnosis: Valvifera with narrow, elongate body. Four anterior

[19]

pairs of peraeopods unlike the three posterior pairs, being directed towards buccal area and provided with plumose setae. Last three pairs of peraeopods adapted for clinging to tubular object, terminal claw or dactyl bifid. Mandible lacking palp. (modified from Richardson, 1905; p. 323; and Nordenstam, 1933, p. 115).

GENUS: *ASTACILLA* Cordiner, 1795

Type species: Astacilla longicornis (Sowerby) *re* G. O. Sars, 1897, pp. 87-88.

Richardson, 1905, pp. 323-327.

Diagnosis: Cephalon and first peraeonal somite fused more or less completely. Flagellum of second antenna triarticulate and bearing terminal claw. Pleon with only two completely separated somites. Apex of first peraeopod with claw. Fourth peraeonal somite much longer than third. Endopod of uropod with apical setae. (Modified after G. O. Sars, 1897, with correction of Nordenstam, 1933).

It is not certain that the species described below belongs to *Astacilla*, and it is quite possible that several species now presently referred to *Astacilla* belong in different and even new genera. The family and the genus require revision before new genera can be characterized and assigned. The *type species* of *Astacilla* has several plumose apical setae on the uropodal endopod. The species described below has only one.

SPECIES NO. 1

Astacilla lauffi, n. sp.

Fig. 1

Synonyms: None

Diagnosis: *Astacilla* with smooth body, having few granulations. First pleonal somite clearly separated from remainder of pleon. The other pleonal somites are completely fused. Terminal pleonal somite with lateral angular expansions near proximal margin and lesser posterolateral angles near distal margin; apex pointed.

Measurements: Holotype female length 5 mm (without antennae); width at widest part 2 mm.

Distribution: Known from type locality and from the following stations off Georgia.

Material Examined: Sta. 283, one male, one juvenile; Sta. 280, two females, one juvenile; Sta. 293, one specimen; Sta. 360, one female; Sta. 362, one male; Sta. 363, one female; Sta. 364, two females.

Type Locality: 30° 47′ 56″ N; 80° 00′ 15″ W; 441 feet, Sta. 360. *Affinities*: This species appears to be closely related to *Astacilla granulata* (Harger, 1878, *vide* Richardson, 1905, pp. 324-325) and bears a general resemblance to *Neastacilla californica* (Boone) (Menzies and Barnard, 1959, Fig. 18). It differs from *A. granulata* in lacking granulation on the dorsum and from *N. californica* in having the anterolateral angles of the pleotelson much larger than the posterolateral angles instead of being subequal in size.

This species cannot belong to *Neastacilla* because the apical article of the first peraeopod bears a claw. It may not belong to *Astacilla* because the endopod of the uropod bears a single apical seta, and the pleon differs from the type species of *Astacilla* in being shorter and in possibly having fewer fused somites.

Disposition of Type Specimen: The holotype female has been deposited in the collections of the U. S. National Museum, Cat. No. 111077; allotype, U. S. National Museum, Cat. No. 111080.

FAMILY: IDOTEIDAE

Diagnosis: Valvifera with body generally somewhat depressed. First pair of antennae often shorter than second pair, flagellum with single long article and few or no apical articles. First pair of peraeopods usually stout and similar to other peraeopods. Pleonal somites variously coalesced. First peraeonal somite always distinct from cephalon. Uropoda usually uniramous (modified after Richardson, 1905; Menzies, 1962b).

GENUS: *EDOTEA* Guerin-Meneville, 1843

Diagnosis: Palp of maxilliped with three articles. Flagellum of second antennae rudimentary, consisting of single thick article with minute apical article. Coxal plates not visible in dorsal view on any peraeonal somite. Pleon composed of single somite plus lateral incisions of another partly coalesced somite. All legs similar. Genital apophyses concealed by operculiform first uropods. Uropods uniramous. (Modified from Richardson, 1905, p. 394).

[21]

Composition: This genus has three species from the East Coast of North America, *E. acuta* Richardson, *E. triloba* (Say), and *E. montosa* (Stimpson), and one species, *E. sublittoralis* Menzies and Barnard, from the West Coast.

SPECIES NO. 2
Edotea montosa (Stimpson)
Fig. 2

Reference: Richardson, 1905, pp. 397-398, Figs. 443-444.
Diagnosis: *Edotea* without projecting horn-like preocular lobes. Lateral margins of peraeonal somites each rounded instead of straight. Incisions at margin of pleon deep and distinct. First pair of antennae extending to middle of last peduncular article of second antennae. Peraeonal somites lack tubercles on dorsum.
Distribution: Grand Manan Is. to Long Island Sound (Richardson, 1905). This record extends the range to Blackbeard Island, Georgia.
Material Examined: Sapelo Island, two males, three young; Blackbeard Island, one male, one young; Sapelo Island, High Point Beach, on oysters, one specimen; Sapelo Island Beach, low water, eight specimens; Sapelo Island Beach, one specimen; Blackbeard Creek, Blackbeard Island, one specimen.
Affinities: This species appears closely related to the Pacific species *Edotea sublittoralis* Menzies and Barnard from which it differs mainly in having a more pointed pleotelson and a lesser development of the preocular horns. The male stylus of the second pleopod of these two species should be carefully compared. To assist in the comparison, we have provided an illustration of this structure for *E. montosa*.

GENUS: *CLEANTIS* Dana, 1852

Diagnosis: Body linear. Coxal plates marked off from peraeon on all but first somite. Pleon with more than one somite. Flagellum of second antenna with a large proximal article usually with a few minute terminal articles at apex. Maxilliped palp with five articles. Uropoda biramous (after Nordenstam, 1933).
Composition: Only one species, *C. planicauda*, is known from the East Coast of the United States. This species has uniramous instead of biramous uropods. Otherwise, it is clearly a member of *Cleantis*.

[22]

SPECIES NO. 3
Cleantis planicauda Benedict
Fig. 3

Reference: Benedict *in*: Richardson, 1899, p. 851 (footnote).
Diagnosis: *Cleantis* with uniramous uropods. Flagellum of second antenna consists of single clavate article without minute apical articles. Dorsum of pleotelson with dish-like impression near apex.
Distribution: Puerto Rico to Florida (Richardson, 1905). This collection extends the range northward to Georgia.
Material Examined: Sta. 4, one male; Sta. 31, 11 adults, Doboy Sound, one gravid female; Sapelo Beach, one young male.
Type Locality: Pensacola, Florida; Richardson, 1899, p. 851.
Affinities: This species of *Cleantis* is distinct from the South American species, *C. linearis* and *C. chilensis*, in having uniramous uropods. It is not known how closely *Cleantis planicauda* is related to the Pacific species *C. occidentalis* Richardson. In gross aspect the two are similar, but because Richardson indicates only four articles to the maxillipedal palp of *C. occidentalis*, it is possible that they are not closely related. Richardson's specimens should be re-examined. The uropods should also be examined to determine the number of rami in the Pacific species.

GENUS: *ERICHSONELLA* Benedict

Synonym: *Ronalea* Menzies and Bowman, 1956, pp. 339-343.
Diagnosis: Flagellum of second antennae consists of a single clavate article. Palp of maxillipeds composed of four articles. Coxal plates of peraeonal somites separated from somites two through seven inclusive. Pleon consists of a single somite but has weak indications near the base of a fused added somite or, in the case of one species, a distinct lateral incision.

Here it is possible to unite *Erichsonella* and *Ronalea*. The presence of lateral incisions at the base of the pleotelson in *Ronalea* and their absence in *Erichsonella* does not seem to be a "good" generic character. This is due to the fact that the specimens of *Erichsonella* examined by us show a reasonably clear groove in dorsal view representing the coalesced somite. In previous works this somite has not been noted.
Composition: Only two species of *Erichsonella* are known from

[23]

the Atlantic coast of North America: *E. filiformis* (Say) and *E. floridana* Benedict. The former species has been subdivided into two subspecies by Menzies (1951).

SPECIES NO. 4

Erichsonella filiformis filiformis (Say)

Fig. 4

References: Richardson, 1905, pp. 401-403. Menzies and Bowman, 1956; Menzies, 1951.

Diagnosis: *Erichsonella* with third and fourth peraeonal somites expanded dorsally to conceal coxal plates. Dorsum of cephalon with trituberculate bump (appears bifid). All peraeonal somites bear median dorsal tubercle near posterior border.

Distribution: Massachusetts to Bahamas (Richardson, 1905).

Material Examined: Sta. 4e, one gravid female; Sta. 189, one male.

Affinities: This subspecies is closely related to *E. filiformis isabellensis* Menzies from the Gulf of Mexico. It may also be very closely related to *E. floridana* Benedict and even *E. crenulata* Menzies, 1950. A very interesting problem in isopod speciation may be revealed through study of an adequate collection of the "species" of this genus.

GENUS: *CHIRIDOTEA* Harger, 1878

Diagnosis: Palp of maxilliped with three articles. Sides of cephalon usually incised. Second antenna with multiarticulate flagellum. Coxal plates separate on all peraeonal somites except first. Pleon with four somites and lateral incisions indicating a partly coalesced fifth. First three pairs of peraeopods subchelate, remaining pairs ambulatory. Uropoda biramous. (Modified from Richardson, 1905, and Bowman, 1955).

Composition: For reference to the systematic position of *Chiridotea* see Nordenstam (1933, pp. 104-110). The biramous uropoda, the incised lateral margin of the cephalon, the subchelate anterior peraeopods, and the number of somites of the pleon ally *Chiridotea* to *Macrochiridothea*. The coxal plate development of *Macrochiridothea*, and its quadriarticulate maxillipeds (instead of triarticulate) are characteristics which distinguish

[24]

595.37 M529h
c,1

the two. Because of the affinities stated above, it is our opinion that *Chiridotea* and *Macrochiridothea* are much more closely related than Nordenstam suggests. A close relationship between these two genera has also been postulated by Ohlin (1901).

Nordenstam (1933, p. 110) holds to the view of Racovitza and Sevastos (1910) that *Macrochiridothea* is more closely related to *Glyptonotus* than to *Mesidothea*. On this matter we have no opinion.

Nordenstam contended in his familial diagnosis of the *Macrochiridothinae* that the maxillipedal palp was triarticulate. Menzies (1962b) shows a quadriarticulate maxillipedal palp for the type species *Macrochiridothea stebbingi* Ohlin, 1901. Apparently the small basal article of the maxillipedal palp was not noted by Ohlin (1901).

SPECIES NO. 5
Chiridotea caeca (Say)
Fig. 5

Reference: Richardson, 1905, pp. 353-354.

Diagnosis: *Chiridotea* with lateral margin of cephalon deeply incised and with produced preocular region whose lateral margin extends as far as the lateral margin of the postocular lobes. Angle between lateral lobes of cephalon acute. First and second antennae subequal in length. Eyes present but obscure. Second antennae extending only to anterior margin of first peraeonal somite, margin of apex of pleon with minute teeth. Front of cephalon not deeply incised at frontal margin.

Distribution: Nova Scotia to Florida; Richardson, 1905, p. 353.

Material Examined: Sapelo Island, Beach, one male; Blackbeard Creek, one male; Sta. 207, one juvenile.

Affinities: This species appears to be quite closely related to *Chiridotea arenicola* Wigley (1960) and *C. nigrescens* Wigley (1961). Wigley points out that *C. caeca* can be distinguished from *C. arenicola* by its larger size, broader peraeopods, thicker and more convex body, broader pleotelson, and its longer and more setiferous antero-lateral sections of the head. *C. caeca* can be distinguished from *C. nigrescens* by its larger size, lighter color, deeper clefts in the antero-lateral margin of head, and its greater setation on the margins of the cephalon and epimera.

[25]

SPECIES NO. 6
Chiridotea stenops, sp. nov.
Fig. 6

Reference: None

Diagnosis: Lateral margin of cephalon not deeply incised; almost entire, preocular region narrow in comparison with the produced postocular region, frontal margin not deeply set in. Lateral margin of apex of pleotelson with only three to five setae. First antenna longer than peduncle of second. Eyes reduced, almost obscure. Color ranges from blackish to nearly white.

Distribution: Known only from type locality.

Material Examined: Station 200, four specimens; Station 201, five specimens.

Measurements: Male holotype length 2.3 mm; width 1.0 mm.

Type Locality: Off Georgia, 31° 06′ -09′ N; 80° 32′ -37′ W; 85-96 ft., M. Gray and D. Darby, Forster Dredge - 5/6/63.

Affinities: This species appears to be unique in having the lateral margins of the cephalon almost entire rather than being deeply cleft and distinctly bilobed. Thus this species does not appear to be very closely related to any of the others which have been described.

Disposition of Types: The holotype has been deposited in the collection of the U. S. National Museum, Cat. No. 11075.

FAMILY: BOPYRIDAE

Only one bopyrid was found in the collections. It appears related to *Pseudione curta* (Richardson) but certain problems make this determination uncertain. Accordingly, we have not assigned it to a species and are uncertain even of the generic assignment.

SPECIES NO. 7

GENUS: *PSEUDIONE* ? Kossmann, 1881

Reference: Richardson, 1905, pp. 495-583.

One species of isopod from the branchial chamber of a snapping shrimp was in the collections. We present illustrations of this animal even though we have been unable to determine its specific identity.

[26]

The male resembles *Pseudione curta* Richardson 1904, (*re.* 1905, pp. 530-531) to some degree but the female is quite unlike that figured by Richardson (1905, Fig. 574), in that it lacks peraeonal appendages from one side. We suspect that we are dealing with a new genus but hesitate to attempt to describe this form. More specimens are required to determine precisely the segmentation of the female.

FAMILY: CYMOTHOIDAE

Diagnosis: Cirolanoidea with all seven pairs of peraeopods prehensile. Pleopoda without plumose setae in adults. Maxillipedal palp composed of two articles with the terminal article with stout claw-like setae. Antennae reduced, not elongated and without a clear distinction between peduncle and palp (modified after Richardson, 1905, p. 214).

Four genera of these fish parasites were encountered in the collections: *Aegathoa, Lironeca, Cymothoa,* and *Olencira.*

GENUS: *AEGATHOA* Dana, 1852

Diagnosis: Cymothoidae with cephalon produced posteriorly into three lobes. Eyes large and conspicuous. Uropoda and apex of pleotelson with delicate fringe of plumose setae. Pleon not abruptly narrower than peraeon. (After Richardson, 1905, pp. 215-216).

Composition: Only three species have been described from the East Coast and Caribbean. As Richardson (1905) points out, this genus may be only juveniles of *Lironeca* or other cymothoid genera. This conclusion remains likely because to our knowledge a gravid female *Aegathoa* has never been collected. The rearing of the young *Lironeca* to maturity should solve the problem. Menzies, Bowman, and Alverson (1955) have shown that the young of *Lironeca* meet the characteristics of the family *Aegidae* as they develop from the free swimming "larva" to maturity.

SPECIES NO. 8
Aegathoa oculata (Say)
Fig. 8
Reference: Richardson, 1905, pp. 217-219.
Diagnosis: *Aegathoa* with a rounded and entire frontal margin to

the cephalon, lacking special lingulate projections. Dorsal surface of cephalon smooth, evenly convex. Second pair of antennae composed of ten articles. Peraeonal appendages bear stout setae along inferior margin. (After Richardson, 1905, pp. 216-218).

Distribution: Connecticut to St. Thomas, West Indies (Richardson, 1905).

Material Examined: Blackbeard Island, Beach, one male; Sapelo Island, Beach, six specimens (two small specimens from *Bairdiella chrysura*); Dean Creek, one specimen.

Type Locality: Savin Rock near New Haven, Conn. (Richardson, 1905).

Affinities: This species is quite distinct from the other two American species in having a smooth evenly convex cephalon with no lingulate projections.

Remarks: This species has been found parasitic on the squid, *Loligo pealii*, and the mullet. In these collections it was either free living or found on the sand perch, *Bairdiella chrysura*.

GENUS: *LIRONECA* Leach, 1818

Diagnosis: Body suboval, more or less twisted to one side. Cephalon usually deeply immersed in first peraeonal somite. Pleonal lateral margin usually continuous with lateral margin of peraeon except for first or second pleonal somites which may be narrow and immersed. Peraeopods lack stout setae on inferior margins. (Modified from Richardson, 1905, p. 256).

Composition: This genus is represented by three species along the East Coast of the United States: *L. redmanni, L. ovalis* and *L. texana*. Here we report a fourth species.

Monod (1931) is followed in the use of *Lironeca* instead of *Livoneca*. The latter spelling appears to have been a typographical error.

SPECIES NO. 9
Lironeca reniformis sp. nov.
Fig. 9

Reference: None

Diagnosis: *Lironeca* with first pleonal somite narrower than second, reaching only to posterolateral margin of last peraeonal somite. Uropodal exopod wider than endopod, rami subequal in length. Front of cephalon rounded. Pleotelson 1.6 times as wide

[28]

as long, rounded posteriorly. Cephalon set into first peraeonal somite more deeply on left side than on right.

Measurements: Holotype male, length 7 mm; width 3.5 mm.

Distribution: Known only from type locality.

Material Examined: Sta. 42, one male.

Type Locality: Off Georgia, 31° 03′ N; 80° 11′ W; 144 feet, M. Gray, Sta. 42.

Affinities: This species may be distinguished from both *Lironeca ovalis* and *L. redmanni* by the narrow first pleonite and from *Lironeca redmanni* by the shortness of the uropods which do not extend beyond the pleonal terminal margin.

Lironeca reniformis appears to be closely related to *L. texana* (Pearse, 1952), but can be distinguished from this species by the distinctive shape of the first peraeonal somite and by the shape and dimensions of the pleotelson. In *L. reniformis* the cephalon is set into the first peraeonal somite more deeply on the left side than on the right whereas in *L. texana* the two sides are set in equally. In *L. reniformis* the pleotelson is 1.6 times as wide as long, and is widest near the anterior margin. In *L. texana* the pleotelson is two times as wide as long, and the posterior margin is curved inward in female specimens and in male specimens the pleotelson is widest halfway down its length.

In the light of these differences we are describing this species as new although future comparisons of *L. texana* and *L. reniformis* should be made to assure this designation.

Disposition: The holotype is deposited in the collection of the United States National Museum, Cat. No. 111076.

GENUS: *CYMOTHOA* Fabricius, 1793

Diagnosis: Body ovate, lacking a twist to right or left. Cephalon usually deeply immersed in first peraeonal somite. First peraeonal somite longer than other somites. Pleon deeply immersed in last peraeonal somite, pleonites increase in width from front to rear. Pleotelson quadrate in shape. (Modified after Richardson, 1905, p. 247).

Composition: The Eastern seaboard inclusive of the Caribbean has three species, *C. excisa* Perty, *C. caraibica* Bovallis and *C. oestrum* (Linnaeus). The first mentioned species was found in the collections.

[29]

SPECIES NO. 10
Cymothoa excisa Perty
Fig. 10

Reference: Richardson, 1905, pp. 248-250.

Diagnosis: Anterolateral angles of first peraeonal somite acute, extend half the length of the cephalon or less. Uropoda shorter than pleotelson.

Distribution: Massachusetts to Brazil (Richardson, 1905).

Material Examined: Dean Creek, Sapelo Island, Georgia; one male.

Affinities: This species is distinguished from *C. exigua* Schioedte and Meinert from Panama by having the anterolateral angles of the first peraeonal somites sharply angular and extending to the middle of the cephalon. The two species appear to be closely related.

GENUS: *OLENCIRA* Leach, 1818

Diagnosis: Cephalon constricted at base, not immersed in first peraeonal somite. Pleotelson triangular. Uropoda lanceolate, much shorter than pleotelson. Peraeopods lack stout setae from inferior margin. Seventh peraeopods distinctly longer than any of first six.

Composition: Only one species of *Olencira* is known and it was represented in the collections.

SPECIES NO. 11
Olencira praegustator (Latrobe)
Fig. 11

Reference: Richardson, 1905, pp. 231-233.

Diagnosis: *Olencira* with cephalon elongate and subtrapezoidal in shape; eyes large, elongate located in post-lateral angles of cephalon. First and fourth pleonal somites longest and sub-equal; coxal plates distinct on pleonal somites two through seven, not reaching posterior margin of pleonal somites. Rami of uropods subequal, pointed, not reaching apex of pleotelson.

Distribution: Maryland to Florida; Richardson, 1905.

Material Examined: Dean Creek, Sapelo Island, Ga.; one male, one female, on *Brevoortia tyrannus*. Doboy Sound, two specimens.

Affinities: This is the only species of *Olencira* known to science and thus is unique.

[30]

FAMILY: SEROLIDAE

Diagnosis: Flabellifera with the fourth and fifth pairs of pleopods large, indurated, and operculiform, first through third pleopods normal, smaller than fourth and fifth. Cephalon united medially with the first peraeonal somite. Body flattened, strongly depressed. Uropods small, normal, not arching over pleotelson. (After Menzies, 1962b).

This family and its genus *Serolis* have not previously been recorded from the Atlantic coast of North America. At least one species appears to be present.

GENUS: *SEROLIS* Leach, 1814

Diagnosis: *Coxal* plates marked off from terga of second through fourth peraeonal somites only. Third article of maxillipedal palp well developed. Lappets of outer lobe on second pair of maxillae provided with a small number of setae. Basipods of first three pairs of pleopods each provided with setiferous triangular extension at inner proximal angles. Endopod of third pleopod entire. (After Nordenstam, 1933, p. 50).

Composition: Only one species was known previously from the northern hemisphere, *Serolis carinata* Lockington from California and Mexico. These collections add another which also represents the first serolid known from the North Atlantic.

SPECIES NO. 12
Serolis mgrayi sp. nov.
Fig. 12.

Diagnosis: Serolis with briamous uropoda, rami flattened, subequal in length. Coxal areas of peraeonal somites not extending beyond apex of pleotelson. First and second antennae subequal in length. Uropoda extending slightly beyond apex of pleotelson. Dorsum of cephalon with two spine-like tubercles on midline. All peraeonal somites except fifth bear a median tubercle at posterior margin; second through fourth peraeonal somites with a spine-like tubercle at posterolateral corner.

Measurements: Holotype, length 4.0 mm; width (at widest part) 3.0 mm.

Distribution: Known from type locality and from the following stations off Georgia.

[31]

Material Examined: Sta. 264, one male; Sta. 282, one specimen; Sta. 284, one specimen; Sta, 286, two specimens; Sta. 320, one juvenile; Sta. 325, one specimen.

Type Locality: Off Georgia. 31° 20′ 22″ N; 80° 00′ 26″ W, Forster Dredge, M. Gray, male holotype.

Affinities: Except for the lateral spine-like tubercles in peraeonal somites two through four, this species resembles *S. carinata* from California and Mexico. The two species should be carefully compared to assure their distinct or conspecific nature. We have provided a detail of the gnathopodal (first peraeopod) setae to assist this comparison by future workers.

This species is named in honor of Mr. Milton Gray whose careful collections provided the stimulus for this study.

Disposition of Types: The holotype is deposited in the collections of the United States National Museum, Cat. No. 111071.

FAMILY: ANTHURIDAE

Diagnosis: Flabellifera with tubular and elongate bodies over five times as long as wide. Uropods often arching over pleotelson. Statocysts frequently present on pleotelson. Mouth parts adapted for chewing, piercing, and sucking. First pair of peraeopods subchelate. (Modified from Richardson, 1905).

Six genera were present in the collections, only two of which had been known previously from the Atlantic Coast of North America. One genus appears to be new to science.

GENUS: *PTILANTHURA* Harger, 1878

Diagnosis: Eyes developed but small (even in adult male). Peraeon with dorsal pits. Pleon rather long, segments distinct. First antenna with brush-like flagellum in male, pauciarticulate in female. Second antenna with pauciarticulate flagellum in both sexes. Mandible with palp consisting of a single joint. Maxilliped three-jointed. Shape of fifth joint of peraeopods four through seven and other characters uncertain (after Barnard, 1925).

Barnard remarks that he had seen no specimens, and we have determined that the fifth joint of peraeopods four through seven is elongate and does not underride the sixth.

Composition: Barnard listed only one species, *Ptilanthura tenuis*

[32]

Harger, 1878, for this genus. It had been reported from the east coast of North America from 0 to 19 fathoms. The species we report here may or may not belong to *Ptilanthura*. It fits the generic description in most regards but deviates somewhat in two characters. Both this species and the genus *Ptilanthura* belong to group A of Barnard's two groupings within the family Anthuridae. In this species, however, the eyes are large rather than small and the segments of the pleon are not distinct in dorsal view, although slight indications of pleonal somites are evident in lateral view. The first pleopod in the female, and we have seen only females, is operculate and covers the remaining pleopods. We tentatively describe the following as a new species of *Ptilanthura* because we believe it best to keep the forms distinct until sufficient material, including a male of this species, is available for comparison with Harger's description of *P. tenuis.*

SPECIES NO. 13
Ptilanthura tricarina sp. nov.
Figs. 13, 14A

Reference: None.
Diagnosis: Eyes large, laterally situated. Front of cephalon with a slight median point between the antennae. First antenna reaching to the last peduncular article of the second antenna. Flagellum of first antenna consisting of two articles, first article about three times the length of second. Flagellum of second antenna with four articles, and second article 1.5 times the length of first and longer than any of the following articles. First, second, and third peraeonal somites subequal in length; third, fourth, and fifth subequal in length; seventh about one-half the length of sixth. Pleon (less pleotelson) subequal in length with the sixth segment of peraeon. Exopod of uropod extending slightly beyond one-half the length of pleotelson. Endopod of uropod extending nearly to the apex of the pleotelson. Pleotelson with three carinae running along the length of its dorsal surface and indurated. Medial carinae extending the entire length of pleotelson. Six pleonal somites show clearly in lateral view of pleon. Fourth article of seventh peraeopod not overriding fifth article. Maxilliped consisting of three articles (according to Barnard's definition). Mandible with a single article to the palp terminating in two fairly stout setae. Gnathopod without any large spines but with ten

[33]

marginal setae on the inferior margin of the sixth article. Lateral margin of uropodal exopods crenulate.

Measurements: Holotype length 5.8 mm; width 0.5 mm.

Distribution: Known from the type locality and from the following stations off Georgia.

Material Examined: Sta. 229, one female; Sta, 251, one female; Sta. 277, one juvenile; Sta. 281, one female; Sta. 290, one specimen; Sta. 292; one specimen; Sta. 293, one specimen; Sta. 305, two females; Sta. 308, one juvenile; Sta. 311, one female; Sta. 316, one female; Sta. 324, one female; Sta. 332, one female; Sta. 359, one female; Sta. 362, two juveniles.

Type Locality: Off Georgia. 31° 20-50′ N; 79-81° W; 93 ft., bucket dredge, M. Gray, one female holotype.

Affinities: This species appears related to *Ptilanthura tenuis* Harger (Richardson, 1905, p. 67). It differs markedly from this species by the following characteristics. First, the pleon lacks any indication of dorsal segmentation. Second, the dorsum of the pleotelson is provided with very obvious carinae which are so characteristic that they form the basis for the name of the species. It is important that males of this species be compared with males of *Ptilanthura tenuis* to discern the differences that might exist. We have not had access to male specimens in these collections.

Disposition of Type: The holotype has been deposited in the collection of the United States National Museum, Cat. No. 111082.

GENUS: *CYATHURA* Norman and Stebbing, 1886

Diagnosis: Eyes usually present. Peraeon typically with dorso-lateral keel and dorsal pits. First antenna with flagellum one through three jointed, usually brush-like in male. Second antenna with single jointed flagellum. Mandible with third joint of palp usually larger than first, with a rather large apical tuft of setae. Maxilliped four-jointed (counting a basal joint anchylosed to head). First peraeopod with a tooth on palm of sixth joint, unguis usually long. Peraeopods two and three with cylindrical sixth joint. Peraeopods four through seven with fifth joint under-riding sixth. Pleopod one and uropods not indurated. Exopod of uropod usually folding over telson. Oostegites three pairs. (Modified from Norman and Stebbing, 1886, *vide* Miller and Burbanck, 1961, p. 65).

[34]

SPECIES NO. 14
Cyathura polita (Stimpson)
Fig. 14B

Reference: Miller and Burbanck, 1961; Barnard, 1925.

Diagnosis: Eyes small. Anterolateral angles of cephalon subequal in length with the rounded median rostral point. Mandible with 13 or 14 stout setae on third article of palp; 14-18 serrations on cutting flange. Maxilla one with one large and six small apical teeth. Maxilliped three-jointed with a coalesced basal piece. Peraeopod one not sexually dimorphic. Propodus of peraeopod six with length four times its width. Pleonites one through five fused dorsally but occasionally with a lateral suture between pleonites one and two, and rarely with indications of additional lateral sutures. Dorsally the pleon bears paired lengthwise sutures which diverge anteriorly, ending in a circular area. Sixth pleonite free along anterior border; posterior border fused to pleotelson on each side of middorsal line; partial suture along middorsal line at point of fusion. Pleopod two with terminal complex of appendix masculina not extending beyond apical edge of endopod. Hook-crowned rod originating some distance from base of lateral lobe, hooks extend one-fourth the length of the rod. Distal end of appendix masculina extends beyond end of hooked rod. Uropods with exopods 0.3 to 0.4 as wide as long, distal margins widely separated dorsally and without distinct incisions. Telson with sides subparallel anteriorly, converging strongly posteriorly. (After Miller and Burbanck, 1961).

Distribution: Atlantic and Gulf Coasts of United States from Maine to Louisiana (Miller and Burbanck, 1961).

Material Examined: Sapelo Island, High Point Beach, 17 specimens; five males, 12 females.

Type Locality: Chesapeake Beach, Maryland.

Affinities: This species is closely related to *Cyathura carinata* with which it had been considered synonymous previous to Miller and Burbanck's (1961) revision. It differs from this species most markedly in the obvious fusion of the sixth pleonite with the pleotelson and in the structure of the appendix masculina. The species also appears to be closely related to *Cyathura burbancki* from which it differs in the relationship of the rostral projection and the anterolateral angles of the cephalon, in the obvious fusion of the sixth pleonite to the pleotelson, and in the width of the

[35]

uropodal exopodites, as well as in other more subtle features summarized by Frankenberg (1965).

SPECIES NO. 15
Cyathura burbancki Frankenberg
Fig. 14C

Reference: Frankenberg, 1965.

Diagnosis: Eyes small. Antero lateral angles of cephalon extend
further anteriorly than the truncated median rostral projection.
Mandible with eight to ten stout setae on third article of palp;
17 to 20 serrations on cutting flange. Maxilla one with one large
and five small apical teeth. Maxilliped three-jointed with a coalesced basal piece. Peraeopod one often more robust in female than
in male. Propodus of peraeopod six with length five times its
width. Pleonal somites one through five fused dorsally but with
distinct lateral suture between first and second pleonal somites
and often between second and third. Two dorsal sub-parallel
sutures on the pleon diverge anteriorly and often are continuous
with the lateral suture between first and second pleonal
somites. Sixth pleonal somite free along entire anterior and
posterior borders, posterior border deeply incised mid-
dorsally. Second pleopod with terminal complex of appendix
masculina not extending beyond apical edge of endopod.
Hook-crowned rod originating some distance from base
of lateral lobe, hooks extend one-third the length of the rod.
Distal end of appendix masculina extends beyond end of hooked
rod. Uropods with exopods 0.5 to 0.7 as wide as long, distal
margins often meet and sometimes overlap dorsally, and are
incised. Telson widest halfway down its length, sides converge
slightly anteriorly, strongly posteriorly.

Distribution: Known from type locality and from the following
stations off Georgia.

Type Locality: Off Georgia. 31° 19′ 15″ N., 81° 07′ 45″ W.

Material Examined: Sta. 276, one specimen; Sta. 305, two specimens; Sta. 335, four specimens; Sta. 337, two specimens; Sta.
340, one specimen; Blackbeard Island, one specimen.

Affinities: This species is closely related to *Cyathura polita*. A
discussion of this relationship is included with the affinities of
C. polita and in Frankenberg (1965). *Cyathura burbancki* also
appears to be related to *C. carinata* from which it differs markedly
in the structure of the appendix masculina, in the relationship of

[36]

the dorsal and lateral sutures of the pleon, and in the absence of a middorsal suture on the pleotelson. The apparent close relationships of *C. burbancki, C. polita,* and *C. carinata* bring up interesting questions concerning the evolution of these forms, and a comparison of the physiology of these species might prove rewarding.

SPECIES NO. 16

GENUS: ACCALATHURA ? Barnard, 1925
Fig. 14D

Reference: Barnard, 1925, pp. 147-149.

One species of juvenile anthurid having characteristics near the genus *Accalathura* Barnard was in the collections. Because of its juvenile nature we were unable to place it in *Accalathura* with reasonable assurance of the correctness of that assignment.

The species is illustrated so that future students may be alerted to its presence off the Atlantic coast of North America.

It was collected from off Georgia at Sta. 298 (two juveniles).

GENUS: *XENANTHURA* Barnard, 1925

Diagnosis: Anthuridae belonging to section A of Barnard's (1925) groupings in the family Anthuridae. Eyes present. Peraeon not dorso-laterally keeled, without dorsal pits. Pleon long, segments distinct. Pleotelson greatly reduced, thin, without statocyst. First antenna with flagellum brush-like in male, single-jointed in female. Second antenna with flagellum consisting of several obscurely separated joints. Mandibular palp consisting of a minute article plus an apical seta. Maxillipeds three-jointed. First peraeopod with straight palm, unguis short. Second and third peraeopods also subchelate but a little smaller than first, sixth joint ovate. Fourth through seventh peraeopods very short, fifth joint under-riding sixth. First pleopod not operculiform, no larger than the others, both rami equally developed. Uropods with endopod completely fused with peduncle; exopod large, ovate, closing down over its fellow and over the pleotelson. Oostegites (?). (Modified from Barnard, 1925, p. 138).

The type-species for this genus is *Xenanthura brevitelson* Barnard (1925) from St. Thomas, West Indies, 20 to 30 fathoms. The type is in the Copenhagen Museum. Since that time Pillai

[37]

(1963) has described one additional species *Xenanthura linearis*, and redescribed *X. orientalis*, Barnard. Pallai suggests that the peduncle of the first antennae bears two flagella. We have checked this repeatedly on our specimens without finding any indication of a secondary flagellum. Barnard (1925) also describes two flagella on the first antennae. In this case it appears that a damaged sensory bristle may have been interpreted as a flagellar joint. We have not examined *X. orientalis* Barnard, or *X. linearis* Pillai, so we can make no statement concerning these species, but it seems clear that the occurence of a secondary flagellum is a specific rather than a generic characteristic. Pillai describes species in which eyes are lacking, and this also appears to be a specific characteristic. Perhaps one of the most characteristic features common to all species of this genus is the truncate and very short pleotelson.

SPECIES NO. 17
Xenanthura brevitelson Barnard
Fig. 15

Reference: Barnard, 1925, pp. 138-139.
Diagnosis: Adult male with three pairs of eyes occupying entire lateral margin of cephalon. Frontal projection of cephalon exceeds lateral projection by slight amount. Pleotelson shorter than length of both rami of uropods. Pleotelson convex at distal margin bearing total of four setae on apical margin. Inner two setae swollen, with margin of minute bristles near apex of each. Telson also bearing a pair of minute bristles near apex. All peraeopods somewhat subchelate. First three peraeopods with large projection on inferior margin extending half the length of palm on peraeopods two and three, and one-third the length of the palm in peraeopod one. Flagellum of first antennae with two subequal articles, flagellum of second antennae with six apical articles and stout sensory bristles on last peduncular article which is the longest article of the peduncle. Maxilliped consisting of three articles and a coalesced basal piece, terminal article widest at the middle. First and third somites to peraeon subequal in length; second and fourth longer than first and subequal; fifth, sixth, and seventh subequal in length. First pleonal somite one-half the length of seventh. Second, third, fourth, and fifth pleonal somites subequal in length, sixth slightly shorter than fifth. Exopod of uropods subcircular in out-

[38]

line, transparent. Endopod club-shaped, extending slightly beyond the apical margin of exopod and one-third longer than the telson.

One of the most unusual features of this species is the presence of three pairs of eyes. This characteristic occurs only in the male. The female has only one pair of small eyes.

Measurements: Male, length 4.5 mm; width 0.3 mm.

Distribution: This species was originally described by Barnard from St. Thomas, West Indies, and it has not been collected since that time. These specimens represent a considerable extension of the range from the West Indies to Georgia.

Material Examined: Station 305, one male; Station 344, one specimen; Station 360, one specimen.

Type Locality: St. Thomas, West Indies; 25-30 fathoms.

GENUS: PANATHURA Barnard, 1925

Diagnosis: Belongs in section A of the family Anthuridae (Barnard, 1925). Maxilliped with at least six joints, endite well developed. Palm of first peraepod nearly straight. Eyes minute, laterally located. Front of cephalon with median projection. Mandibular palp triarticulate (modified from Barnard, 1925, p. 143).

Composition: Barnard (1925) mentions only one species in this genus, *Panathura serricauda* from South Africa. Another species is present in these collections and we believe it is new.

SPECIES NO. 18
Panathura formosa sp. nov.
Fig. 16

Reference: None

Diagnosis: Eyes minute, laterally located. First antenna with flagellum two-jointed. Mandible with first and third palpal joints subequal in length and shorter than second. Pleotelson spatulate, widest at distal two-thirds, apex truncate, lateral margin serrate. Endite of maxilliped with a single seta. Apex of pleotelson with continuous fringe of setae. Apical article of maxillipedal palp with two stout setae.

Measurements: Holotype female (fragment), length 4.5 mm; width 0.3 mm.

Distribution: Known only from type locality.

Material Examined: Station 298, one female (fragmented).

Type Locality: Off Georgia. 31° 26′ 32″ N; 79° 42′ 13″ W;

[39]

291-252 ft., Tumbler Dredge, M. Gray. One female holotype, fragmented.

Affinities: This species may be distinguished from *Panathura serricauda* (Barnard) by having only two setae at the apex of the maxillipedal palp instead of six or more and in having a continuous fringe of setae at the apex of the pleotelson instead of two groups of setae which are separated at the midline. In addition, the palm of *P. formosa* has a small stout spine plus several setae on the margin in contrast to the "perfectly straight and entire margin" on the palm of *P. serricauda* (Barnard, 1920, pp. 339-340).

Disposition of Type: The holotype has been deposited in the collections of the United States National Museum, Cat. No. 111081.

GENUS: *APANTHURA* Stebbing, 1900

Diagnosis: Eyes usually present, absent in the deep water species. Peraeon segments not pitted. Pleon with sutures distinct. Pleotelson not indurated, rather thin, dorsally smooth and convex. First antenna with flagellum of one joint or obscurely, two to three-jointed, or occasionally brush-like in male. Second antenna with flagellum rudimentary. Mandible with third palpal joint shorter than or subequal to first, sometimes with a comb of setae, sometimes with only an apical tuft. Maxilliped five-jointed. First peraeopod usually with a tooth on palm near base, unguis typically long. Second and third peraeopods with sixth somewhat ovate. Fourth through seventh peraeopods with fifth joint underriding sixth. First pleopod not indurated. Uropods not indurated, exopods folding over pleotelson. Oostegites four pairs (*A. xenocheir, apud* Stebbing). (Modified after Barnard, 1925, p. 141).

Composition: Barnard (1925) lists five species and two others have been described, one by Miller and Menzies (1952) from Hawaii and the other by Schultz (1964) from California. One species present in the collections from Georgia appears to be new.

SPECIES NO. 19
Apanthura magnifica sp. nov.
Fig. 17

Reference: None
Diagnosis: Eyes present, large in male and minute in female. First antenna with two-jointed flagellum. Second antenna with

[40]

flagellum brush-like in male, four-jointed in female. First peraeopod with basal tooth on palm. Pleotelson ovate, apex pointed in female, subtruncate in male. Uropod with endopod nearly twice as long as broad and not narrower than peduncle, exopod broadly ovate, apex notched. Color pale yellow to white, without pigmentation; eyes black.

Measurements: Holotype female, length 8.5 mm; width 0.75 mm.

Distribution: Known from the type locality and from the following stations off Georgia.

Material Examined: Station 1-A, five specimens; Station 189, one specimen; Station 202, one male; Station 242, one specimen; Station 246, one specimen; Station 280, one specimen; Station 281, one specimen; Station 316, one specimen; Station 320, one specimen; Station 322, one specimen; Station 323, one specimen; Station 339, one specimen; Station 359, one specimen.

Type Locality: Off Georgia. 30° 48' 05″ N; 80° W; Station 359, 461 feet, bucket dredge, M. Gray. One female holotype.

Affinities: In the character of the brush-like male antennal flagellum this species differs from all other species in the genus *Apanthura* except for *A. senegalensis* (Barnard, 1925, p. 143). It differs from *A. senegalensis* in lacking a setal comb on the mandibular palp. *Apanthura magnifica* also appears to be distinctive in showing only a partial dorsal separation between the fourth and fifth pleonal somites. The palmar surface of the gnathopod is very close to *A. inornata* (Miller and Menzies, 1952).

Disposition of types: The holotype has been deposited in the collection of the United States National Museum, Cat. No. 111073.

GENUS: *HOROLOANTHURA*, gen. nov.

Type-species: *Horoloanthura irpex* sp. nov.

Diagnosis: Anthuridae belonging to section A of Barnard's (1925) two sections within the family. Eyes absent. Mouth parts normal; statocysts probably absent; unguis on first peraeopod short; pleotelson neither splayed nor indurated. Fifth article of fourth through seventh peraeopods underriding sixth. First pleopod not operculiform, similar to remaining pleopods. Maxilliped with five articles. All pleonal somites distinctly separated from each other. Sixth somite of peraeon the largest. Length of

[41]

pleon (including pleotelson) equals the length of the last two peraeonal somites combined.

This genus is close to *Hyssura* Norman and Stebbing, 1886 (*vide* Barnard, 1925). A main point of difference is in the fourth through seventh peraeopods which in *Horoloanthura* have the fifth article underriding the sixth. In *Hyssura* the fifth and sixth articles are much longer than wide and neither underrides the other. Otherwise the genera are similar.

One species of *Horoloanthura* was found in the collections.

SPECIES NO. 20
Horoloanthura irpex gen. et. sp. nov.
Fig. 18

Diagnosis: *Horoloanthura* with a sharply pointed pleotelson. Uropodal rami reach to apex of pleotelson, exopod elongate, bluntly pointed and with three stout teeth on exterior margin. Exopod arching over pleon. Flagellum of first antenna with three articles. Flagellum of second antenna with seven articles. First antenna half the length of second antenna.

Measurements: Holotype female, length 3.7 mm; width 0.2 mm.

Distribution: Known from the type locality and from the following stations off Georgia.

Material Examined: Station 359, one female; Station 366, one female.

Type Locality: Off Georgia. 30° 45′ N; 80° 02′ W; 285 feet, bucket dredge, M. Gray, one female holotype.

Disposition of types: The holotype female has been deposited in the collections of the United States National Museum, Cat. No. 111074.

FAMILY: SPHAEROMIDAE

Diagnosis: Flabellifera with three somites to pleon plus indications of one or more added partial somites on middle one. Mandibular molar truncated and broad. Body usually shortened, not more than two times as long as broad. Cephalon always separated from first peraeonal somite.

The family is separated into three reasonably distinct groups by the structure of the pleopods. In the platybranchiate group none of the pleopods are fleshy or have transverse folds. In the

[42]

hemibranchiate group the endopods of the fourth and fifth pleopods are fleshy and have transverse folds. In the eubranchiate group both the endopods and the exopods of the fourth and fifth pleopods are fleshy and have transverse folds.

This family was represented by four genera and five species.

GENUS: *ANCINUS* Milne-Edwards

Diagnosis: Platybranchiate Sphaeromidae with first peraeopod subchelate; second peraeopod of male prehensile, of female ambulatory. Mandible lacks a molar process. Uropod without exopod; endopod fused to sympod into a single styliform appendage. Second pleopod operculate.

Composition: Two species of the genus *Ancinus* are known from the coasts of the United States. *Ancinus daltonae* (Menzies and Barnard, 1959) occurs on the Pacific Coast, and *A. depressus* (Say) occurs along the Atlantic and Gulf Coasts. The latter species was present in the collections studied here.

SPECIES NO. 21
Ancinus depressus (Say)
Fig. 19

Reference: Richardson, 1905, pp. 271-272.

Diagnosis: *Ancinus* with uropods pointed and reaching the apex of pleon. Appendix masculina of male second pleopod not reaching apex of endopod. Rostral process on cephalon bluntly pointed and equal in width to one-half the length of the first peduncular article of the first antenna.

Distribution: Known previously from Egg Harbor, New Jersey (Richardson, 1905), Woods Hole, Massachusetts (Richardson, 1909), and the Texas coast (Pearse, 1952). This is the first report of this species from the Southeastern Atlantic Coast of the United States.

Material Examined: Off Georgia. Station 126, two males; Wolf Island, Georgia, beach, one male.

Affinities: This species appears closely related to *Ancinus daltonae* Menzies and Barnard (1959) from the coast of California. The two species differ mainly in that *A. daltonae* has larger uropods which are quite broad and extend beyond the apex of the pleotelson by one-third their length. In *A. depressus* the uropods just reach to the apex of the pleotelson.

[43]

GENUS: *CASSIDINIDEA* Hansen, 1905

Synonyms: *Cassidisca* Richardson, 1905, p. 272.
Dies Barnard, 1951, p. 701

Diagnosis: A transitional member of the Sphaeromidae with rami of fourth and fifth pleopods fleshy and unjointed but lacking transverse folds. Uropodal exopod minute and inserted into expanded lateral margins of sympod and endopod. Outer margin of exopod participates in continuous border of lateral margin of uropod. Lobes of maxillipedal palp not produced on inner margin. Peraeopods all similar and ambulatory. Eyes situated at posterolateral corners of cephalon. (modified from Richardson, 1905, pp. 272-273).

Composition: As noted by Barnard (1951) for *Dies monodi*, the pleopods in this genus are clearly intermediate in structure between the "Platybranchiate Sphaeromidae" and the "Hemibranchiate Sphaeromidae" of Hansen (1905). Two species are known from the Atlantic coast of the United States. One was found in the collections.

It is highly probable that *Dies* Barnard (1951) and *Cassidisca* Richardson are synonyms and except for the single penial process of *Dies* as compared with the double process on *Cassidisca* they appear identical. As noted by Richardson (1905) *Cassidisca* is a synonym of *Cassidinidea* Hansen.

SPECIES NO. 24
Cassidinidea lunifrons (Richardson)
Fig. 20

Reference: Richardson, 1905, pp. 273-274.

Diagnosis: *Cassidinidea* with dorsum of pleotelson smooth, without low transverse elevations at base. Uropodal exopod one-fourth as long as endopod. Apex of pleotelson truncate (modified from Richardson, 1905, p. 273).

Distribution: Previously this species was known from New Jersey (Richardson, 1905) to North Carolina (Wells, 1961). These specimens extend the range southward to Georgia.

Material Examined: Georgia, Sapelo Island marsh in mud and dead leaves. North Carolina at Beaufort, several specimens, R. Heard.

Affinities: This genus is represented by only two species on the Atlantic Coast of the United States. *Cassidinidea lunifrons* can be distinguished from *C. ovalis* by the shape and ornamentation of

[44]

the pleotelson, and by the relative lengths of the uropodal rami. In *C. lunifrons* the dorsum of the pleotelson is smooth and the apex is truncate while in *C. ovalis* the dorsum has a low transverse elevation and the apex is triangulate. Also, in *C. lunifrons* the uropodal exopods are one-fourth as long as the endopods whereas in *C. ovalis* the exopods are one-third to one-half as long as the endopods.

GENUS: *EXOSPHAEROMA* Stebbing

Diagnosis: Hemibranchiate Sphaeromidae lacking a slender mesial process on last peraeonal somite of male. Apex of pleotelson of both sexes similar, not produced, and without an obvious groove on the lower side at apex. (after Menzies, 1962b, p. 132). *Composition*: Only one species of *Exosphaeroma* was present in the collection. Richardson (1905) recorded *Exosphaeroma faxoni* from Florida but this species has been transferred to *Cymodoce* by Menzies and Miller (1955). In addition Richardson (1905) recorded *E. crenulata* Richardson from Bermuda. The latter species is the one that we might expect to occur in Georgia.

SPECIES NO. 23
Exosphaeroma diminutum sp. nov.
Fig. 21

Reference: None
Diagnosis: *Exosphaeroma* with uropoda not quite reaching to apex of pleotelson. Cephalon wider than long, with short median tubular rostrum. First somite of peraeon 1.5 times as long as any of the others. Margin of uropodal exopod smooth, not crenulate. Appendix masculina of second male pleopod lanceolate, just reaching apex of margin of endopodite.
Measurements: Holotype length 2.2 mm; width 1.0 mm.
Distribution: Known only from the type locality.
Type Locality: Sapelo Island, Georgia, beach, M. Gray, one holotype.
Material Examined: Sapelo Island Beach, one male holotype, M. Gray, collector.
Affinities: This species is close to *Exosphaeroma crenulatum* Richardson but has entire urodal rami that are not crenulate. In addition the peraeonal somites are not subequal in length, instead, the first is longer than the others. One cannot be sure of the validity of these distinctions and actual specimens should be com-

pared. *Exosphaeroma diminutum* does not appear to be closely related to *E. papillae* Bayliff from the northeastern coast of the United States since the pleotelson in the two species is quite different. In *E. papillae* the pleotelson is roughly triangular with only a very short lateral margin whereas in *E. diminutum* the pleotelson is distinctly 5-sided with a lateral margin about $\frac{1}{4}$ the length of the segment. *Exosphaeroma diminutum* is minute and appears to be a member of the sand beach biota.

Disposition of type: Holotype deposited in the collections of the U. S. National Museum, Cat. No. 111078.

GENUS: *PARACERCEIS* Hansen, 1905

Diagnosis: Eubranchiate Sphaeromidae with seventh peraeonal somite without median mid-dorsal projection. Apex of pleotelson incised in male and with a tubular ventral channel in female. Uropodal exopod of male about two times the length of endopod (sympod); these rami are subequal in the female. Dorsum of pleon usually with ornamentations.

Composition: Along the Atlantic coast this genus has two species which Richardson (1905) had assigned to *Cilicaea*, but which she reassigned to "Hansen's new genus *Paracerceis*" (page IX). These are *P. caudata* (Say) and *P. carinata* Richardson. Only the former species was found in the collections.

SPECIES NO. 22
Paracerceis caudata (Say)
Fig. 22

Reference: Richardson, 1905, pp. 314-318.

Diagnosis: *Paracerceis* in which male has pleotelson with cordiform foramen at apex, two sharp stout teeth below this foramen on midline, and bifid postero-lateral projections. In addition, male specimens have uropodal endopod short and pointed. Dorsum of pleotelson with five stout tubercles (one on midline with a pair on either side), and medial section of pleon with transverse row of three tubercles. Female specimens have three low tubercles on dorsum of pleotelson. Uropodal rami subequal in length not reaching posterior margin of pleotelson, and apex of pleotelson scarcely incised.

Distribution: New Jersey to Yucatan, Mexico (Richardson, 1905).

Material Examined: Georgia. Sta. 46, two females; Sta. 68, one female; Sta. 69, one female; Sta. 108, one male; Sta. 132, two fe-

[46]

males; Sta. 128, one male; Sta. 189, seven females, one male; Sta. 198, 33 females, four males; Sta. 199, one female; Sta. 205, one male; Sta. 272, one female.

Affinities: This species appears closely related to *P. sculpta* (Holmes) (*vide* Menzies 1962c) from lower California. It differs from that species in that the uropodal endopod of the male is pointed instead of strap-like and the pleotelsonal foramen lacks the median sharp spine. The exterior margin of the uropodal exopod in *P. sculpta* is smooth while in *P. caudata* it is irregular.

GENUS: *SPHAEROMA* Latreille

Diagnosis: Hemibranchiate Sphaeromidae with the end of the pleotelson rounded or somewhat produced, mouth parts similar in both sexes, maxillipedal palps with conspicuous lobes, exopods of third pleopods not jointed, and mandibles with normal molar process.

Two species of *Sphaeroma* were encountered; both had been reported from the Atlantic coast previously.

SPECIES NO. 25
Sphaeroma quadridentatum Say
Fig. 23A

Reference: Richardson, 1905, pp. 281-282.

Diagnosis: *Sphaeroma* lacking tuberculations from dorsum of pleon and pleotelson. Uropods extending to apex of rounded pleotelson and with rami subequal in length. Exopod of uropod with four stout teeth. Posterior margin of pleotelson marginally elevated.

Distribution: New England to Southern Florida (Richardson, 1905). The type locality is St. Catherine's Island, Ga.

Material Examined: Sapelo Island, Georgia, beach pilings; 66 specimens.

Affinities: This species appears to be unique in having the pleon and pleotelson smooth, without tuberculations.

SPECIES NO. 26
Sphaeroma destructor Richardson
Fig. 23B

Reference: Richardson, 1905, pp. 282-286.

Diagnosis: *Sphaeroma* with dorsum of pleon and pleotelson tuberculate. Last somite of peraeon with transverse row of four

[47]

tubercles. Middle somite of pleon with two stout tubercles. Pleotelson with four stout tubercles in a transverse row on proximal third of pleotelson. Remainder of pleotelson with about seven transverse rows of small tubercles. Pleotelson apically more pointed than rounded. Rami of uropods pointed and extending beyond apical margin of pleotelson; exopod with four or five stout marginal teeth.

Affinities: This species appears to be closely related to *Sphaeroma pentodon* which occurs on the Pacific Coast of the United States. *Sphaeroma destructor* differs from *S. pentodon* in the number and arrangement of tubercles of the seventh peraeonal somite and the pleon and in lacking a prominent transverse ridge near the apex of the pleotelson. In *S. destructor* there are four tubercles on the seventh peraeonal somite, two on the first pleonal somite, and four in a transverse row on the pleotelson. In *S. pentodon* there are no tubercles on either the seventh peraeonal or the first pleonal somite, and there are eight tubercles on the pleotelson arranged in two longitudinal rows of four each. Richardson (1905, pp. 280-287) discusses the relationships of these species to others in the genus, and presents rather cogent arguments for the validity of *S. destructor* as a distinct species.

Distribution: St. Johns River, Florida (Richardson, 1905). These specimens extend the range northward to Georgia.

Material Examined: Sapelo Island, Georgia, Raccoon Bluff, hard pan, 16 specimens.

FAMILY: CIROLANIDAE

Diagnosis: Flabellifera with body no more than two times as long as wide. Pleon with six distinct somites. Molar process of mandible knife-like and provided with teeth on cutting edge. Uropoda not arching over pleotelson, usually lateral and sometimes ventral. Peraeopods usually ambulatory and similar to each other in structure. (Modified after Richardson, 1905, p. 81). Two genera, *Eurydice* and *Cirolana*, were present in the collections.

GENUS: *EURYDICE* Leach

Synonym: *Branchuropus* Moore, 1902.

Diagnosis: Cirolanidae with peduncle of second antennae with four articles. First antennae with basal article of peduncle ex-

[48]

tended straight in front at right angles to remainder of antennae. Opposing basal articles meet at midline of cephalon. Pleon with six somites. Uropoda provided with plumose setae, and insert on ventral side of pleon. (Modified after Richardson, 1905, p. 123).

Two species of this typically planktonic genus were found in the collections.

SPECIES NO. 27
Eurydice littoralis (Moore)
Fig. 24

Reference: Richardson,, 1905, pp. 128-130.

Diagnosis: Eurydice with uropods concealed below pleon, pleopod-like in structure. Apex of pleotelson with fringe of four stout pointed setae and some plumose setae, margin crenulate. Stout setae always much larger than the crenulations. Body color usually uniformly purple or brown.

Distribution: Puerto Rico (Richardson, 1905). These specimens extend the range northward to Georgia.

Material Examined: Sta. 202, one specimen; Sta. 246, three specimens; Sta. 247, one specimen; Sta. 262, two specimens; Sta. 278, one specimen; Sta. 283, one specimen; Sta. 292, one specimen; Sta. 333, one specimen; Sta. 338, one specimen; Sta. 344, two specimens; Sta. 348, one specimen; Sta. 343, one specimen; Sta. 357, one specimen; Sta. 363, one very small specimen.

Affinities: This species appears to be the one described by Moore from Puerto Rico as *Branchuropus littoralis.* The description of the maxilliped appears to have been an error because the maxilliped is normal and not just two small articles, as was previously pointed out by Menzies and Barnard (1959). The species appears closely related to *Eurydice branchuropus* Menzies and Barnard from the California coast. The principal difference is in the strength of the pleotelsonal carinae along the midline on the upper third of the pleotelson, but this is a minute difference and the two need to be carefully compared. They may be conspecific.

SPECIES NO. 28
Eurydice piperata sp. nov.
Fig. 25

Reference: None

Diagnosis: Eurydice with uropods concealed below pleon, pleopod-like in structure. Apex of pleotelson with a fringe of four stout

[49]

setae and some plumose setae, margin crenulate. Stout setae not projecting beyond the margin of the crenulations. Body light yellow with few scattered black chromatophores.

Measurements: Holotype female length 5 mm; width 0.7 mm.

Distribution: Known from the type locality and the following stations off Georgia.

Type Locality: Off Ga. 30° 45′ 44″ N; 80° 02′ 13″ W; 309 Ft., bucket dredge, 9/12/63 M. Gray, collector, six specimens.

Material Examined: Sta. 11, one specimen; Sta. 204, two specimens; Sta. 290, one specimen; Sta. 291, one specimen; Sta. 307, five specimens; Sta. 308, one specimen; Sta. 309, one specimen, Sta. 359, three specimens; Sta. 363, one specimen; Sta. 365, six specimens; Sta. 367, seven specimens; Sta. 368, six specimens.

Affinities: This species is closely allied to *E. littoralis* (Moore) from which it differs in having smaller stout setae on the distal margin of the pleotelson and in the color of the body. There appears to be an ecological separation of *E. piperata* from *E. littoralis*, with *E. littoralis* occupying shallower water than *E. piperata*. Because intergrades occur at the juncture of the two ranges it is highly probable that these two are really subspecies. The problem requires added study.

Disposition of types: The holotypes have been deposited in the collection of the United States National Museum, Cat. No. 111079.

GENUS: *CIROLANA* Leach

Diagnosis: Cirolanidae in which the first peduncular article of the first antenna does not project outward at right angles to the remainder of the antenna. Uropoda fan-like, lateral and indurated being unlike the pleopods (modified from Richardson, 1905).

The collections contained two species which have been previously recorded from the Atlantic coast.

SPECIES NO. 29

Cirolana polita (Stimpson)
Fig. 26

Reference: Richardson, 1905; pp. 99-101.

Diagnosis: *Cirolana* with eyes present. Sides of cephalon rounded. Body oblong. Fifth pleonal somite with lateral parts covered by fourth. Frontal lamina narrow and elongate, not produced and

[50]

not horn-like. Extremity of uropodal endopod with a notch on outer margin. Apex of pleotelson with margin entire, provided with plumose setae and minute stout setae.

In contrast with Richardson's key to the genus *Cirolana* (1905, p. 83), the pleotelsonal apex does have several minute stout setae. These show on Harger's illustration (Richardson, 1905, Fig. 80d).
Distribution: Known from Bay of Fundy to Massachusetts (Richardson, 1905). These specimens extend the range southward to Georgia.
Material Examined: Station 293, one specimen; Station 347, one female.
Affinities: The species is easily distinguished from the following one by the notched uropodal endopod.

SPECIES NO. 30

Cirolana parva (Hansen)
Fig. 27
Reference: Richardson, 1905, pp. 111-114.
Diagnosis: *Cirolana* with eyes. Fifth pleonal somite with lateral parts covered by fourth somite. Frontal lamina broad but not produced anteriorly and not horn-like. Apex of pleotelson rounded and armed with stout setae. Second pair of antennae extending to posterior margin of fourth peraeonal somite.
Distribution: Florida, Bahamas and Gulf of Mexico (Richardson, 1905). This specimen extends the range northward to Georgia.
Material Examined: Georgia. Sta. 64, one male.
Affinities: The species is easily distinguished from *Cirolana polita* (Stimpson) by the absence of a notch from the uropodal endopod. It appears to be closely related to *Cirolana diminuta* Menzies from Baja California, Mexico. These two species differ in that the pleotelson is more pointed in *C. diminuta* than in *C. parva*.

[51]

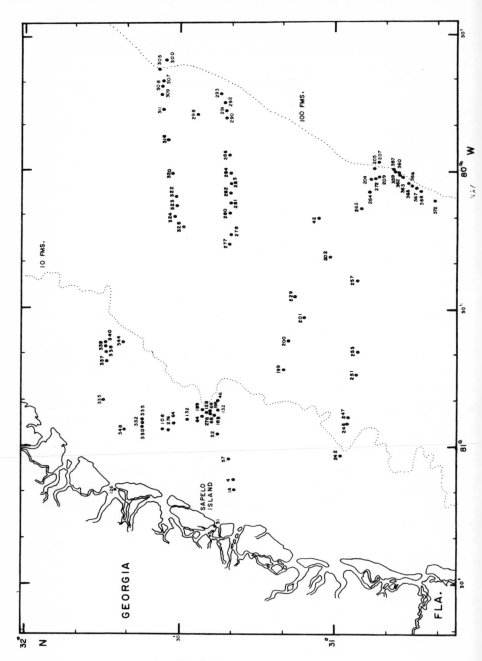

PLATE III. Map of Station Locations

[52]

Station List

Marine isopods were collected off Georgia at the stations given in the following list. These stations are shown on Plate III.

Station 1-A   31° 19' 15" N; 81° 10' 15" W - 63 ft.
              Apanthura magnifica
Station 4   31° 19' 30" N; 81° 08' 15" W
              Cleantis planicauda
Station 31   Doboy Sound
              Cleantis planicauda
Station 42   31° 03' N; 80° 11" W - 144 ft.
              Lironeca reniformis
Station 46   31° 22' 45" N; 80° 49' 51" W - 66 ft.
              Paracerceis caudata
              Erichsonella filiformis filiformis
Station 57   31° 20' 30" N; 81° 03' 30" W - 42 ft.
              Pseudione
Station 64   31° 32' 00" N; 80° 54' 30" W - 58 ft.
              Cirolana parva
Station 68   31° 24' 00" N; 80° 53' 40" W - 55 ft.
              Paracerceis caudata
Station 69   31° 24' 00" N; 80° 53' 00" W - 58 ft.
              Paracerceis caudata
Station 108   31° 34' N; 80° 56' 08" W - 69 feet.
              Paracerceis caudata
Station 126   St. Catherine's Sound, off Walberg Creek
              Ancinus depressus
Station 128   31° 25' N; 80° 53' 15" W - 67 ft.
              Paracerceis caudata

Station 132   31° 27' 45" N; 80° 54' 00" W- 64-70 ft.
Paracerceis caudata

Station 189   31° 25' 30" N; 80° 52' 50" W - 17½ mi at 74°
from "D" 65 ft.
*Apanthura magnifica, Paracerceis caudata, Erich-
sonella filiformis filiformis*

Station 198   31° 23' N; 80° 53' 20" W - 62 ft.
Paracerceis caudata

Station 199   31° 10' N; 80° 43' 15" W; - 81 ft.
Paracerceis caudata

Station 200   31° 09' N; 80° 37' W - 85 ft.
Chiridotea stenops

Station 201   31° 06' N; 80° 32' W - 96 ft.
Chiridotea stenops

Station 202   31° 01' N; 80° 18' 30" W - 115 ft.
Apanthura magnifica
Eurydice littoralis

Station 204   30° 53' N; 80° 01' 30" W - 161 ft.
Eurydice piperata

Station 205   30° 52' 30" N; 79° 59' W - 381 ft.
Paracerceis caudata

Station 207   30° 51' 30" N; 79° 58' W - 341 ft.
Chiridotea sp. indet

Station 229   31° 07' 59" N; 80° 27' 17" W - 93 ft.
Ptilanthura tricarina

Station 242   30° 59' 01" N; 81° 02' 03" W - 57 ft.
Apanthura magnifica

Station 246   30° 57' 36" N; 80° 55' 00" W - 69 ft.
Apanthura magnifica
Eurydice littoralis

Station 247   30° 57' 31" N; 80° 53' 47" W - 77 ft.
Eurydice littoralis

Station 251   30° 56' 00" N; 80° 44' 18" W - 87 ft.
Ptilanthura tricarina

Station 262   30° 55' 04" N; 80° 08' 01" W - 131 ft.
Eurydice piperata

Station 263   30° 47' 31" N; 80° 01' 00" W - 373 ft.
Eurydice piperata

[54]

Station 264   30° 53' 14" N; 80° 04' 15" W - 143 ft.
              Serolis mgrayi
Station 272   30° 52' 02" N; 80° 01' 14" W - 175 ft.
              Paracerceis caudata
Station 276   31° 32' N; 80° 56' 08" W - 70 ft.
              Cyathura burbancki
Station 277   31° 20' 26" N; 80° 16' 00" W - 126 ft.
              Ptilanthura tricarina
Station 278   31° 20' 21" N; 80° 13' 46" W
              Eurydice littoralis
Station 280   31° 20' 18" N; 80° 09' 10" W - 133 ft.
              Apanthura magnifica
              Astacilla lauffi
Station 281   31° 20' 15" N; 80° 06' 57" W - 132 ft.
              Apanthura magnifica
              Ptilanthura tricarina
Station 282   31° 20' 17" N; 80° 04' 44" W - 140 ft.
              Serolis mgrayi
Station 283   30° 20' 21" N; 80° 02' 22" W - 140 ft.
              Eurydice littoralis
              Astacilla lauffi
Station 284   31° 20' 22" N; 80° 00' 26" W - 132 ft.
              Serolis mgrayi
Station 286   31° 20' 27" N; 79° 56' 04" W - 139 ft.
              Serolis mgrayi
Station 290   31° 20' 00" N; 79° 48' 30" W - 189 ft.
              Eurydice piperata
              Ptilanthura tricarina
Station 291   31° 20' 58" N; 79° 46' 38" W - 237 ft.
              Eurydice piperata
Station 292   31° 21' 29" N; 79° 45' 03" W - 301 ft.
              Eurydice piperata
              Ptilanthura tricarina
Station 293   31° 22' 09" N; 79° 43' 08" W - 409 ft.
              Cirolana polita
              Astacilla lauffi
              Ptilanthura tricarina

[55]

Station 298	31° 26′ 32″ N; 79° 42′ 13″ W - 291-252 ft.
	Accalathura juvenile
	Pananthura formosa
Station 305	31° 33′ 44″ N; 79° 37′ 49″ W - 253 ft.
	Cyathura burbancki
	Ptilanthura tricarina
	Xenanthura brevitelson
Station 307	31° 33′ 36″ N; 79° 40′ 21″ W - 213 ft.
	Eurydice piperata
Station 308	31° 33′ 30″ N; 79° 41′ 38″ W - 175 ft.
	Eurydice piperata
	Ptilanthura tricarina
Station 309	31° 23′ 24″ N; 79° 43′ 02″ W - 165 ft.
	Eurydice piperata
Station 311	31° 33′ 13″ N; 79° 46′ 30″ W - 151 ft.
	Ptilanthura tricarina
Station 316	31° 32′ 39″ N; 79° 53′ 04″ W - 145 ft.
	Apanthura magnifica
	Eurydice piperata
	Ptilanthura tricarina
Station 320	31° 31′ 27″ N; 80° 00′ 32″ W - 123 ft.
	Apanthura magnifica
	Serolis mgrayi
Station 322	31° 30′ 31″ N; 80° 05′ 32″ W - 117 ft.
	Apanthura magnifica
Station 323	31° 30′ 46″ N; 80° 07′ 38″ W - 117 ft.
	Apanthura magnifica
Station 324	31° 31′ 02″ N; 80° 09′ 57″ W
	Ptilanthura tricarina
Station 325	31° 29′ 26″ N; 80° 12′ 00″ W - 109 ft.
	Serolis mgrayi
Station 332	31° 37′ 12″ N; 80° 54′ 28″ W - 53 ft.
	Ptilanthura tricarina
Station 333	31° 37′ 12″ N; 80° 54′ 00″ W - 53 ft.
	Eurydice littoralis
Station 335	31° 44′ 55″ N; 80° 49′ 51″ W - 53 ft.
	Cyathura burbancki

Station 337   31° 44′ 17″ N; 80° 41′ 29″ W - 53 ft.
              Cyathura burbancki
Station 338   31° 44′ 03″ N; 80° 39′ 30″ W - 55 ft.
              Eurydice littoralis
Station 339   31° 44′ 07″ N; 80° 38′ 27″ W - 53 ft.
              Apanthura magnifica
Station 340   31° 44′ 11″ N; 80° 37′ 30″ W - 61 ft.
              Cyathura burbancki
Station 344   31° 40′ 52″ N; 80° 27′ 03″ W - 63 ft.
              Eurydice littoralis
              Xenanthura brevitelson
Station 348   31° 40′ 33″ N; 80° 56′ 08″ W - 41 ft.
              Eurydice littoralis
Station 353   31° 01′ 32″ N; 81° 11′ 35″ W - 41 ft.
              Eurydice littoralis
Station 357   30° 48′ 23″ N; 79° 59′ 30″ W - 525 ft.
              Cirolana polita
              Eurydice littoralis
Station 359   30° 48′ 05″ N; 80° 00′ 00″ W - 461 ft.
              Apanthura magnifica
              Eurydice piperata
              Horoloanthura irpex
              Ptilanthura tricarina
Station 360   30° 47′ 56″ N; 80° 00′ 15″ W - 441 ft.
              Astacilla lauffi
              Xenanthura brevitelson
Station 362   30° 47′ 40″ N; 80° 00′ 45″ W - 405 ft.
              Astacilla lauffi
              Ptilanthura tricarina
Station 363   30° 47′ 31″ N; 80° 01′ W - 373 ft.
              Eurydice piperata
              Astacilla lauffi
Station 364   30° 46′ 40″ N; 80° 01′ 30″ W - 343 ft.
              Astacilla lauffi
Station 365   30° 45′ 44″ N; 80° 02′ 13″ W - 309 ft.
              Eurydice piperata
Station 366   30° 45′ 00″ N; 80° 02′ 56″ W - 285 ft.
              Horoloanthura irpex

Station 367   30° 44' 08" N; 80° 03' 28" W - 261 ft.
Eurydice piperata
Station 368   30° 43' 26" N; 80° 04' 02" W - 245 ft.
Eurydice piperata

Distribution

Range Extensions: Ten of the 30 species recorded here were previously known to have a geographic range that included Georgia. Ten species are new to science and our only information about their distribution comes from these collections. Two species lack specific determination. The remaining eight species show extensions of range. Northward extensions include: *Cleantis planicauda* (from Florida), *Xenanthura brevitelson* (from West Indies), *Sphaeroma destructor* (from South Florida), *Eurydice littoralis* (from Puerto Rico), and *Cirolana parva* (from Florida). Southward extensions of range include: *Edotea montosa* (from Long Island), *Cassidinidea lunifrons* (from North Carolina), and *Cirolana polita* (from Massachusetts).

Composition of the Georgia Fauna: From data on isopods little can be said regarding the Georgia fauna except that it appears to contain southern as well as northern elements. It is not known whether any species or genus is endemic but it is doubted that any significant proportions show generic endemism.

Twin or Homologous Species: Dr. Mary Rathbun applied Forbes' concept of twin Atlantic and Pacific species to the decapod Crustacea. The existence of twin species has not yet been recognized for marine isopods. However, because ten of the species in this collection (or 33% of the total fauna) are represented on the Pacific Coast by a comparable species, it is quite likely that this phenomenon requires added attention among the Isopoda and should be studied. The Atlantic species from Georgia that appear to have closely related Pacific twins are:

[59]

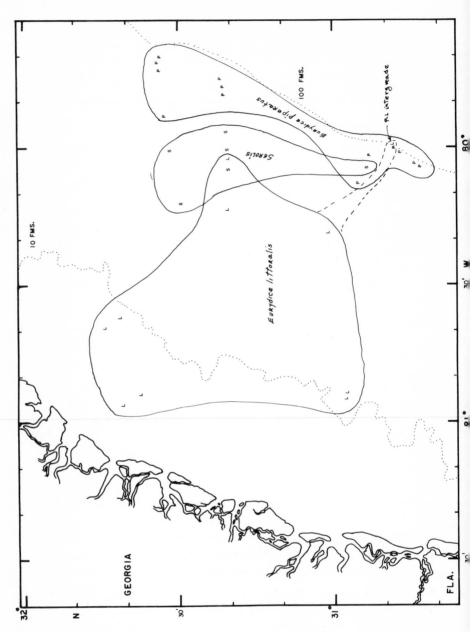

PLATE IV. Distribution of *Eurydice* and *Serolis* in the area investigated
L= *Eurydice littoralis*, S= *Serolis*, P= *Eurydice piperata*. Location of apparent intergrade between L and P, L-P indicated in map

[60]

ATLANTIC	PACIFIC
1. *Edotea montosa* (Stimpson)	*Edotea sublittoralis* (Menzies & Barnard)
2. *Erichsonella filiformis filiformis* (Say)	*Erichsonella occidentalis* Menzies
3. *Cleantis planicauda* Benedict	*Cleantis occidentalis* Richardson
4. *Cymothoa excisa* Perty	*Cymothoa exigua* Schioedte and Meinert
5. *Serolis mgrayi* n. sp.	*Serolis carinata* Lockington
6. *Ancinus depressus* (Say)	*Ancinus daltonae* Menzies and Barnard
7. *Paracerceis caudata* (Say)	*Paracerceis sculpta* (Holmes)
8. *Sphaeroma destructor* Richardson	*Sphaeroma pentodon.* Richardson
9. *Eurydice littoralis* (Moore)	*Eurydice branchuropus* Menzies and Barnard
10. *Cirolana parva* Hansen	*Cirolana diminuta* Menzies

It is interesting to note that all of these twins occur in temperate, subtropical, or even tropical environments instead of boreal or polar conditions. Thus the Pacific twins are from Panama, Mexico or Southern California and the Atlantic twins are from Georgia or points south and north.

Distribution off Sapelo Island, Georgia: It is possible to divide the region sampled into bathymetric zones, e.g. intertidal, shelf (0-100 fms) and shelf break (at 100 fms) but these simple zones do not reflect the character of the botton sediments. Gorsline (1963) and Pilkey and Frankenberg (1964) recognize three sedimentary zones: first, the narrow intertidal and marsh flats; second, a near-shore narrow band of fine sand, silt and detritus; and third, a broad band of coarse sand and shell fragments extending to the shelf break. Isopods were not collected from the second of these zones but they probably occur there. Very few samples were available from this area.

Intertidal Species: Seven species encountered were essentially intertidal in distribution. These are:

1. *Cyathura polita*
2. *Ancinus depressus*
3. *Exosphaeroma diminutum*
4. *Cassidinidea lunifrons*
5. *Sphaeroma quadridentatum*
6. *Sphaeroma destructor*
7. *Chiridotea caeca*

Subtidal Species: The balance of the species were from subtidal collections extending out to the 100 fathom contour.

Parasitic Species: Five species were parasites of fish or crustaceans. These are:

1. *Pseudione* sp. (shrimp)
2. *Aegathoa oculata* (fish)
3. *Lironeca reniformis* (fish)
4. *Cymothoa excisa* (fish)
5. *Olencira praegustator* (fish)

Free Living Species: The remaining species are free living forms. The two species of *Eurydice* appear to be pelagic as well as benthic. The balance of the species are benthic in habit.

Even though the sediments of coarse sand and shell of the broad submerged area do not show any particular added zonation, it is possible to suggest some species zonation. Thus (Pl. IV) shows *Eurydice littoralis* to be generally restricted to the area west of the shelf-break, whereas its near relative *Eurydice piperata* appears to occupy mainly the area at the shelf-break. The genus *Serolis* seems to occupy a band of territory between *Eurydice piperata* and *E. littoralis*, and *Paracerceis caudata* appears to be located in a narrow area between the shore and the area occupied by *E. littoralis*.

Other species either extended broadly over the whole area or were collected so infrequently that distribution patterns could not be determined.

Considerably more work is required to determine the salient features of species distribution off the Georgia coast.

Literature Cited

Barnard, K. H. 1914.
Contributions to the Crustacean Fauna of South Africa - 3 Additions to the Marine Isopoda, with notes on some previously incompletely known species. Ann. of the S. A. Mus. X: 325-442.

Barnard, K. H. 1920.
Contributions to the Crustacean Fauna of South Africa. No. 6. Further additions to the list of Marine Isopods. Ann. of the South African Mus. 17: 319-438.

Barnard, K. H. 1925.
A revision of the family Anthuridae (Crustacea, Isopoda), with remarks on certain morphological peculiarities. Jour. Linn. Soc. Zool. 35: 109-160.

Barnard, K. H. 1951.
New records and descriptions of new species of isopods and amphipods from South Africa. Ann. and Magazine of Natural History, Series 12 IV: 698-709.

Bowman, Thomas E. 1955.
The isopod genus *Chiridotea* Harger, with a description of a new species from brackish waters. Washington Acad. of Sci. 45: (7): 224-229.

Frankenberg, D. 1965.
A new species of *Cyathura* (Isopoda, Anthuridae) from coastal waters off Georgia, U.S.A. Crustaceana. 8(2): 206-212.

Gorsline, D. S. 1963.
Bottom sediments of the Atlantic Shelf and Slope off the southern United States. Jour. Geol. 71: 422-440.

Hansen, J. J. 1905.
On the propagation, structure, and classification of the Sphaeromidae. Quart. Jour. Microsc. Sci. 49: 69-135.

Harger, Oscar. 1878.

Description of new genera and species of isopods from New England and adjacent regions. Amer. Jour. Sci. and Arts XV (3): 373-379.

Harger, Oscar. 1879.

Notes on New England isopods. Proc. U. S. Nat. Mus. II: 157-165.

Menzies, R. J. and Barnard, J. L. 1959.

Marine isopoda on coastal shelf bottoms of Southern Calif., Systematics and Ecology. Pacific Naturalist I (11-12): 3-35.

Menzies, R. J. and Bowman, T. E. 1956.

Emended description and assignment to the new genus *Ronalea* of the Idotheid Isopod *Erichsonella pseudoculata* Boone, Proc. of the U. S. Nat. Mus. 106: 339-445.

Menzies, R. J., Bowman, T. E., and Alverson, F. G. 1955.

Studies of the biology of the fish parasite *Livoneca convexa* Richardson (Crustacea, Isopoda, Cymothoidae). Wasmann J. Biol., Vol. 13, No. 2, pp. 277-295, figs. 1-7.

Menzies, R. J. and Miller, M. A. 1954.

Key to the Chelifera and the suborders of the Isopoda, *in* S. F. Light. Intertidal invertebrates of the Central Calif. Coast, U. Calif. Press: 139-155.

Menzies, R. J. and Miller, M. A. 1955.

Redescription of the marine isopod crustacean *"Exosphaeroma" faxoni* Richardson from Texas. Bul. Mar. Sci. Gulf and Caribbean, 5 (4): 292-296.

Menzies, R. J. 1950.

A remarkable new species of marine isopod. *Erichsonella crenulata* new sp., from Newport Bay, Calif. Bull. So. Calif. Acad. Sci., Vol. XLIX (1): 29-35.

Menzies, R. J. 1951.

A new subspecies of marine isopod from Texas. Proc. U. S. Nat. Mus. 101, (3289): 575-579.

Menzies, R. J. 1953.

The Apseudid Chelifera of the eastern tropical and north temperate Pacific Ocean. Bull. of the Mus. of Comparative Zool., Harvard 107: 443-496.

Menzies, R. J. 1962a

The isopods of abyssal depths in the Atlantic Ocean. Columbia Univ. Press: Vema Res. Ser. (1): 79-206.

Menzies, R. J. 1962b.
The zoogeography, ecology, and systematics of the Chilean marine isopods. Repts. Lund. Univ. Chile Exped. 1948-49, 42: 1-162.

Menzies, R. J. 1962c.
The marine isopod fauna of Bahia De San Quintin, Baja California, Mexico. Pacific Naturalist 3 (11): 338-348.

Miller, M. A. and Burbanck, W. D. 1961.
Systematics and distribution of an estuarine isopod crustacean, *Cyathura polita*, (Stimpson, 1855), new comb., from the Gulf and Atlantic seaboard of the United States. Biol. Bull. 120 (1): 62-84.

Miller, M. A. and Menzies, R. J. 1952.
The isopod crustacea of the Hawaiian Islands, III. Superfamily, Flabellifera, Family Anthuridae. Occ. Pap. Bernice P. Bishop Mus., Honolulu, Hawaii XXI (1): 1-15.

Monod, Th. 1931.
Sur quelques Crustaces aquatiques d'Afrique (Cameroun et Congo) Rev. Zool. Bot. Africaines 21 (1): 1-36.

Nordenstam, Ake. 1933.
Marine isopoda of the Families Serolidae, Idotheidae, Pseudidotheidae, Arcturidae, Parasellidae and Stenetriidae mainly from the South Atlantic. Further Zoological Results of the Swedish Antarctic Expedition, 1901-1903, III (1): 1-284.

Norman, A. M., and Stebbing, T. R. R. 1886.
On the Isopoda of the "Lightning," "Porcupine," and "Valorous," expeditions. Trans. Zool. Soc. London 12: 77-141.

Ohlin, Axel. 1901.
Isopoda from Tierra Del Fuego and Patagonia. 1. Valvifera. Svenska Expeditionen Till Magellansländerna, Bd. II (11): 261-306.

Pearse, A. S. 1952.
Parasitic crustacea from the Texas coast. Publ. Inst. Mar. Sci. Univ. Tex. II (2): 5-42.

Pearse, A. S. and Walker, H. A. 1939.
Two New Parasitic Isopods from the Eastern Coast of North America. Proc. U. S. Nat. Mus., 87: 19-23.

[65]

Pilkey, O. H. and Frankenberg, D. 1964.
The relict-recent sediment boundary on the Georgia continental shelf. Bull. Ga. Acad. Sci. 22 (1): 37-40.

Pillai, N. K. 1963.
Observations on the genus *Xenanthura* (Isopoda, Anthuridae) Crustaceana 5 (4): 263-270.

Racovitza, E. G. and Sevastos, R. 1910.
Proidotea haugi n.g. en. sp. Isopode Oligocene de Roumanie et les Mesidoteini nouvelle sous-famille des Idotheidae. Arch. Zool. Exper. et Gen. Ser. 5, VI.

Richardson, Harriet. 1899.
Key to the isopods of the Pacific Coast of North America, with descriptions of twenty-two new species. Proc. U. S. Nat. Mus. XXI (1175): 815-869.

Richardson, Harriet. 1905.
A monograph on the isopods of North America. Bull. of the U. S. Nat. Mus. 54: 1-717.

Richardson, Harriet. 1909.
The isopod crustacean, *Ancinus depressus* (Say). Proc. U. S. Nat. Mus. 36: 173-177.

Sars, G. O. 1899.
An account of the Crustacea of Norway. Vol. II. Isopoda Bergen Mus., Bergen, Norway: X + 270 pp.

Schultz, G. A. 1964.
Some marine isopod crustaceans from off the southern California coast. Pac. Sci. 28 (3): 307-314.

Stimpson, Wm. 1854.
Synopsis of the marine invertebrates of Grand Manan, on the region about the Bay of Fundy, New Brunswick. Smithsonian Contributions to Knowledge, 1853, VI: 39-44.

Wells, H. W. 1961.
The fauna of oyster beds, with special reference to the salinity factor. Ecol. Mono. 31 (3): 239-266.

Wigley, R. L. 1960.
A new species of *Chiridotea* (Crustacea; Isopoda) from New England waters. Biol. Bull. 119 (1): 153-160.

Wigley, R. L. 1961.
A new isopod, *Chiridotea nigrescens*, from Cape Cod, Massachusetts. Crustaceana 2 (4): 286-292.

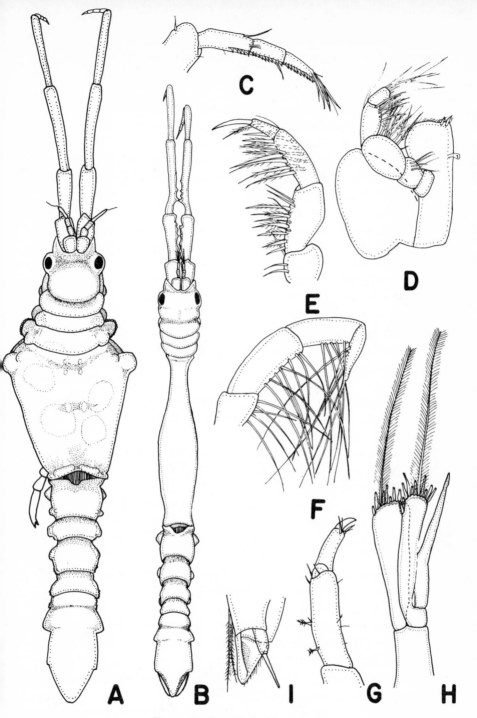

Figure 1. *Astacilla lauffi*, new species

A, whole animal, female (length 8 mm with antennae, 5 mm without antennae; width 2 mm);
B, whole animal, male (length 13 mm with antennae, 8 mm without antennae; width 1 mm);
C, apex of first antenna; D, maxilliped; E, apex of first peraeopod; F, apex of second peraeopod;
G, apex of seventh peraeopod; H, second pleopod of male, with appendix masculina; I, uropod,
lateral view; (C-I drawn from female specimen)

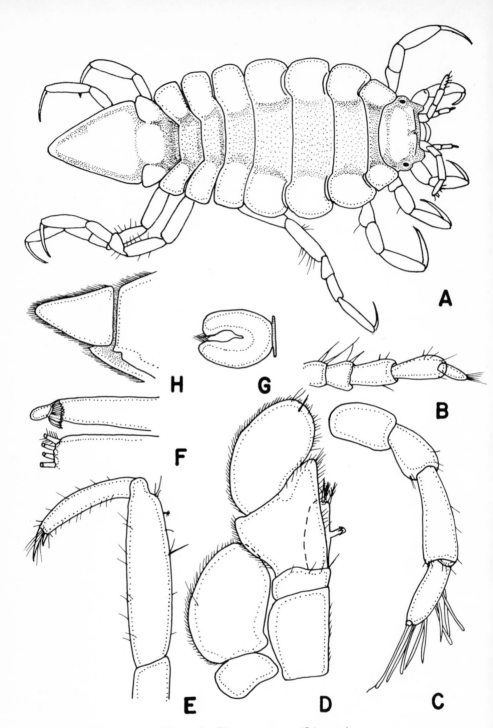

Figure 2. *Edotea montosa* (Stimpson)
A, whole animal, male (length 5 mm. width 2 mm); B, first antenna; C, second antenna;
D, maxilliped; E, apex of sixth peraeopod; F, apex of appendix masculina; G, penes;
H, uropod, lateral view

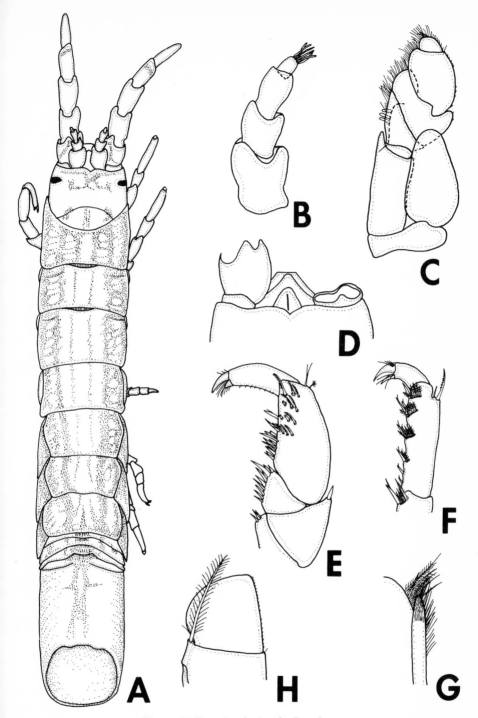

Figure 3. *Cleantis planicauda* Benedict

A, whole animal (length 15.5 mm; width 1.5 mm) ; B, first antenna; C, maxilliped; D, cephalon, ventral view; E, apex of first peraeopod; F, apex of seventh peraeopod; G, apex of appendix masculina; H, apex of uropod

[69]

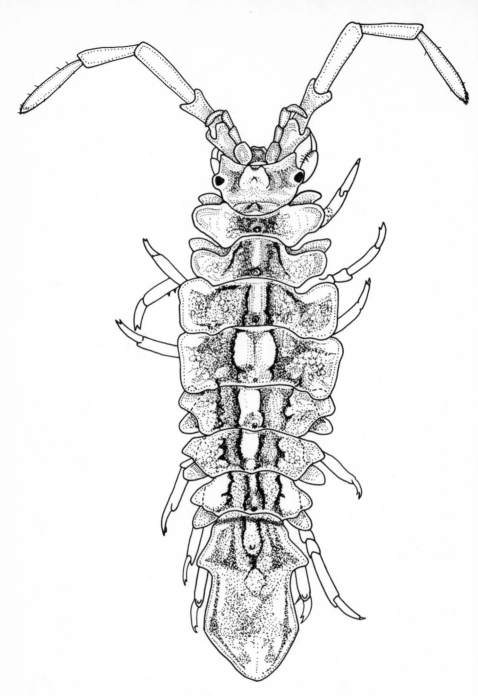

Figure 4. *Erichsonella filiformis filiformis* (Say)
A, whole animal, male (length 12 mm, width 4 mm)

[70]

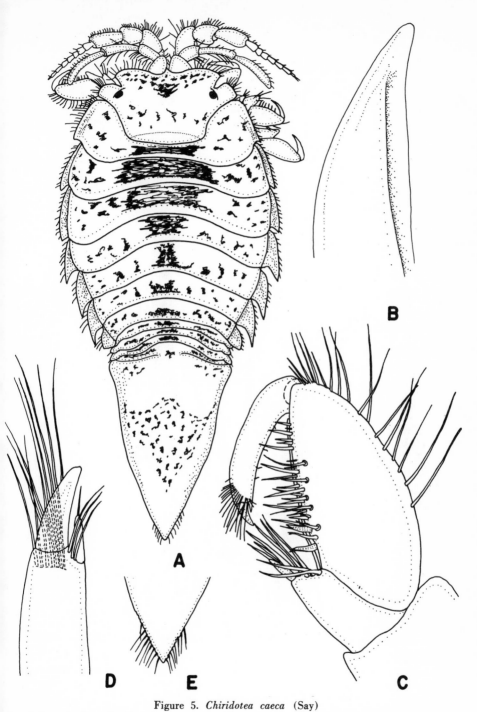

Figure 5. *Chiridotea caeca* (Say)

A, whole animal, male (length 8.5 mm. width 4.0 mm); B, apex of appendix masculinum; C, apex of third peraeopod; D, apex of sixth peraeopod; E, apex of pleotelson

[71]

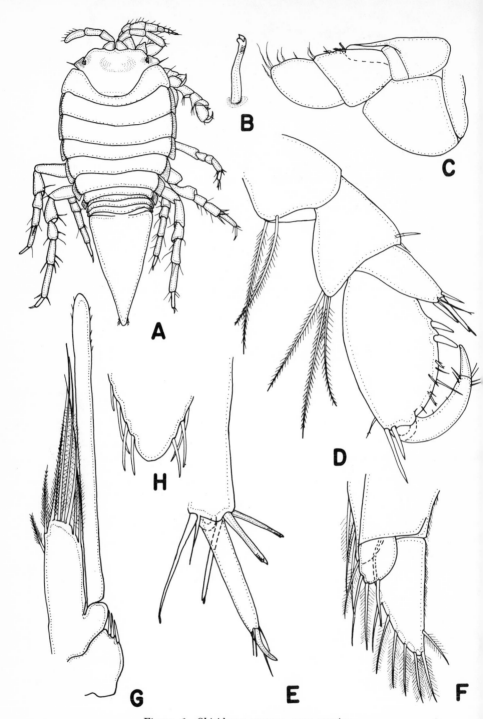

Figure 6. *Chiridotea stenops*, new species

A, whole animal, male (length 2.3 mm, width 1.0 mm); B, seta of first antenna; C, maxilliped; D, apex of third peraeopod; E, apex of sixth peraeopod; F, apex of uropod; G, second pleopod of male, with appendix masculina; H, apex of pleotelson

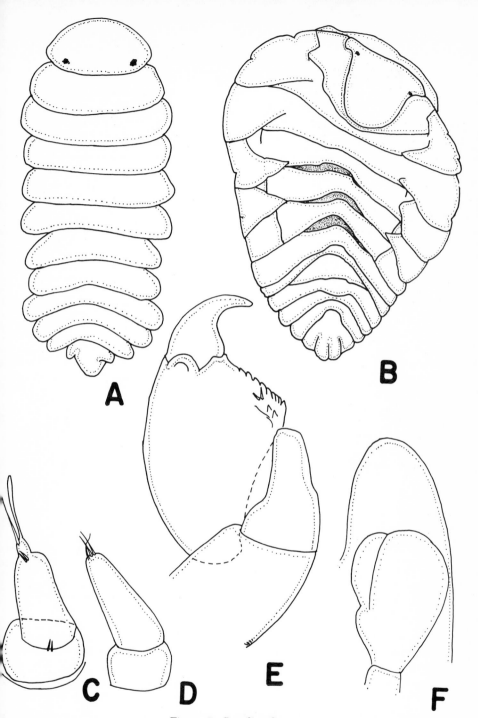

Figure 7. *Pseudione?* sp.

A, whole animal, male; B, whole animal, female (length 7.5 mm; width 5.5 mm); C, apex
of first antenna, male; D, apex of second antenna, male; E, apex of first peraeopod, male;
F, ? lateral margin of ninth somite, male ventral view

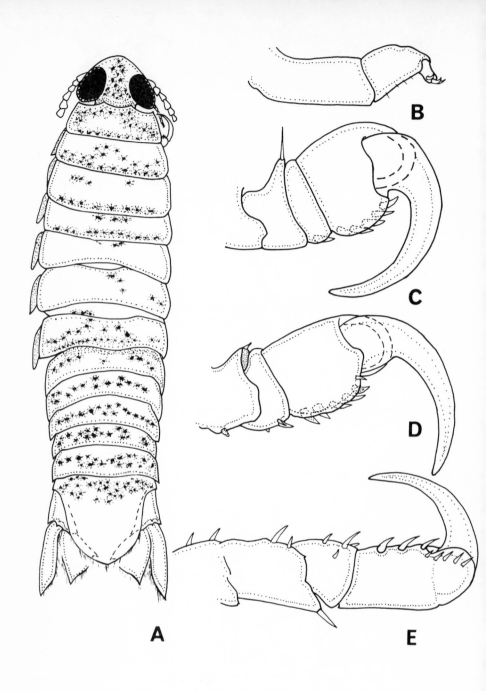

Figure 8. *Aegathoa oculata* (Say)

A, whole animal (length 12 mm, width 3 mm); B, apex of maxilliped; C, apex of first peraeopod; D, apex of fourth peraeopod; E, apex of seventh peraeopod

[74]

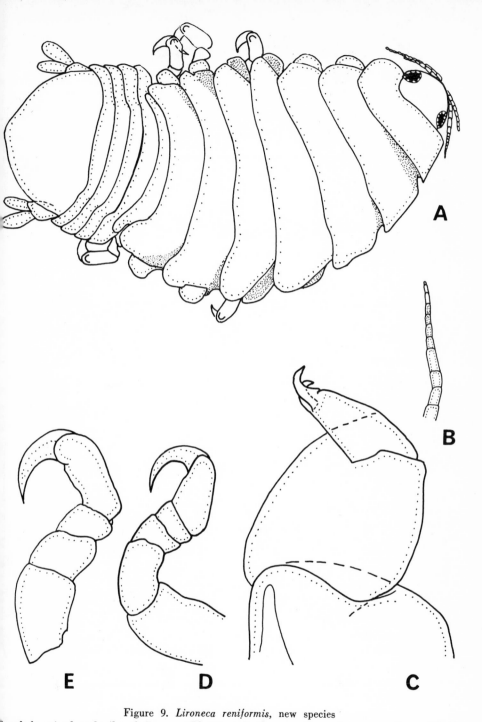

Figure 9. *Lironeca reniformis,* new species

A, whole animal, male (length 7 mm, width 3.5 mm) ; B, apex of second antenna; C, maxilliped; D, apex of first peraeopod: E, apex of seventh peraeopod

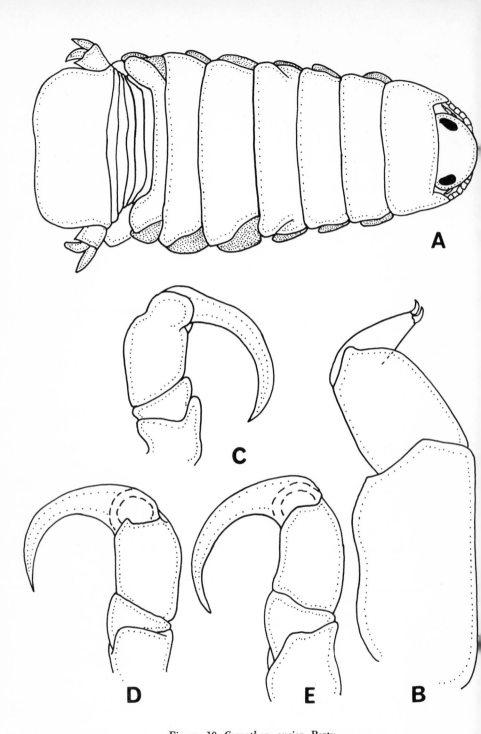

Figure 10 *Cymothoa excisa* Perty
A, whole animal (length 10 mm, width 4.5 mm); B, apex of maxilliped; C, apex of firs
peraeopod; D, apex of fourth peraeopod; E, apex of seventh peraeopod

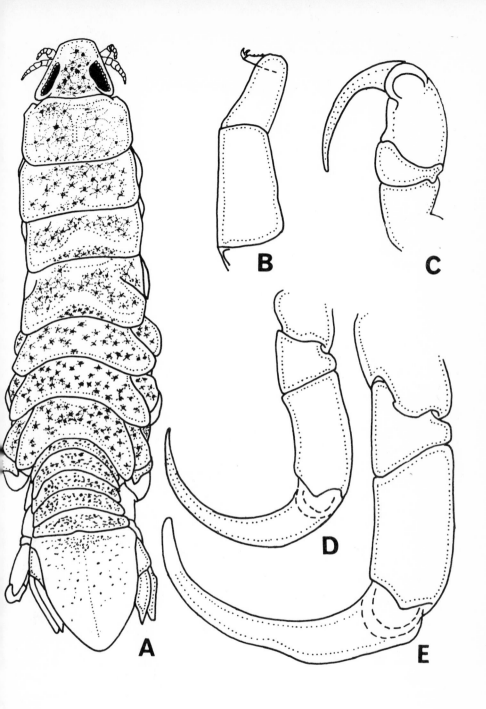

Figure 11. *Olencira praegustator* (Latrobe)
, whole animal (length 23 mm, width 7 mm); B, apex of maxilliped; C, first peraeopod;
, fourth peraeopod; E, seventh peraeopod

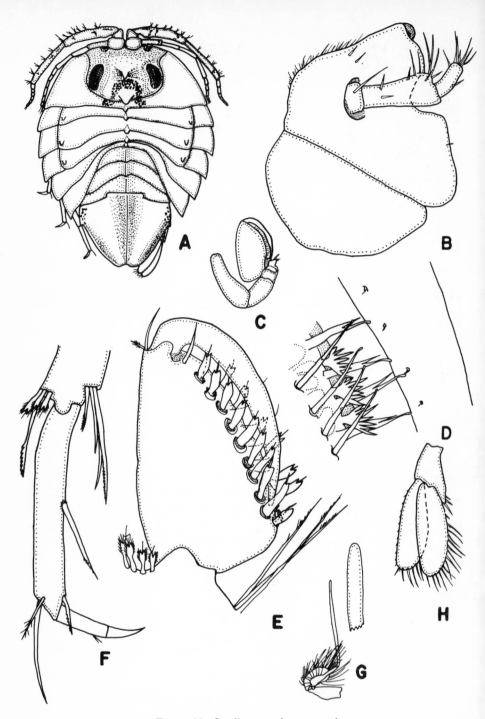

Figure 12. *Serolis mgrayi*, new species
A, whole animal, male (length 4 mm, width 3 mm); B, maxilliped; C, first peraeopod; D, first peraeopod, enlargement of palm and unguis; E, apex of second peraeopod; F, apex of seventh peraeopod; G, second pleopod, with appendix masculina; H, uropod

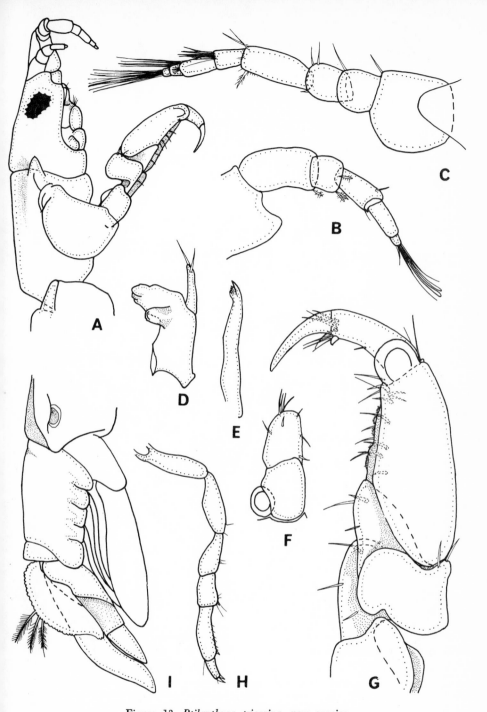

Figure 13. *Ptilanthura tricarina*, new species
A, anterior of female, lateral view, (length of entire animal 5.8 mm, width 0.5 mm); B, first antenna, female; C, second antenna; female; D, mandible; E, first maxilla; F, maxilliped; G, apex of first peraeopod; H, seventh peraeopod; I, posterior of female, lateral view

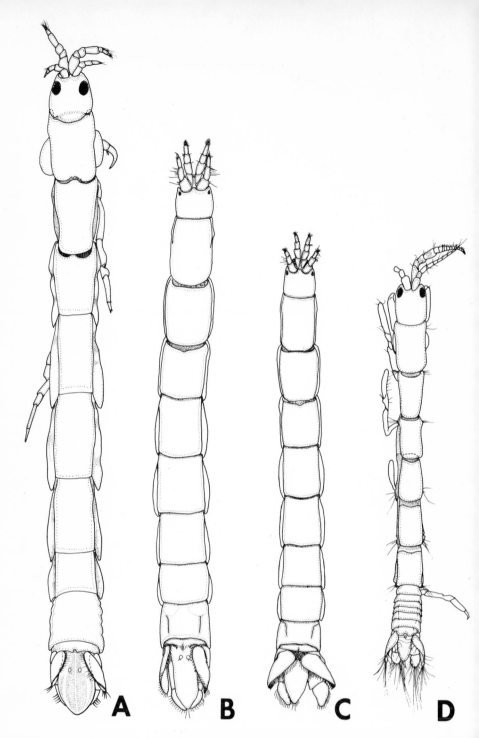

Figure 14. A, *Ptilanthura tricarina*, female (length 5.8 mm, width 0.5 mm); B, *Cyathura polita*, male (length 15 mm); C, *Cyathura burbancki*, male (length 12 mm); D, *Accalathura? crenulata?*, juvenile

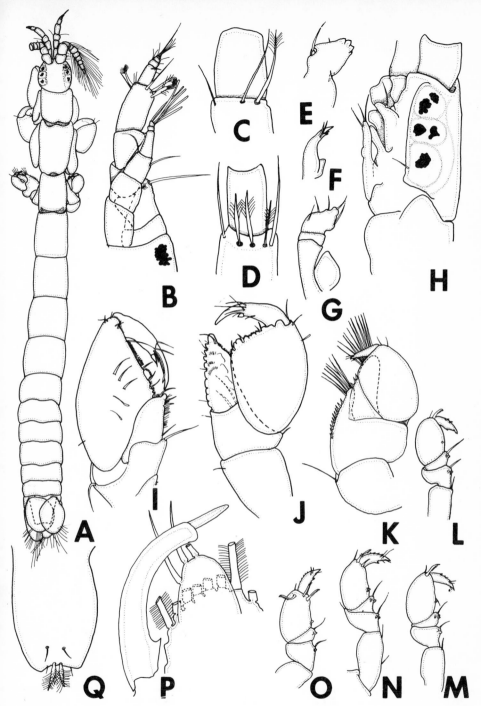

Figure 15. *Xenanthura brevitelson* Barnard

A, whole male (length 4.5 mm; width 0.3 mm); B, antennae, female; C, second antenna, last peduncular segment, dorsal view; D, second antenna, last peducular segment, ventral view; E, mandible; F, first maxilla; G, maxilliped; H, cephalon, male lateral view; I, apex of first peraeopod; J, apex of second peraeopod; K, apex of third peraeopod; L, apex of fourth peraeopod; M, apex of fifth peraeopod; N, apex of sixth peraeopod; O, apex of seventh peraeopod; P, apex of appendix masculina; Q, apex of pleotelson

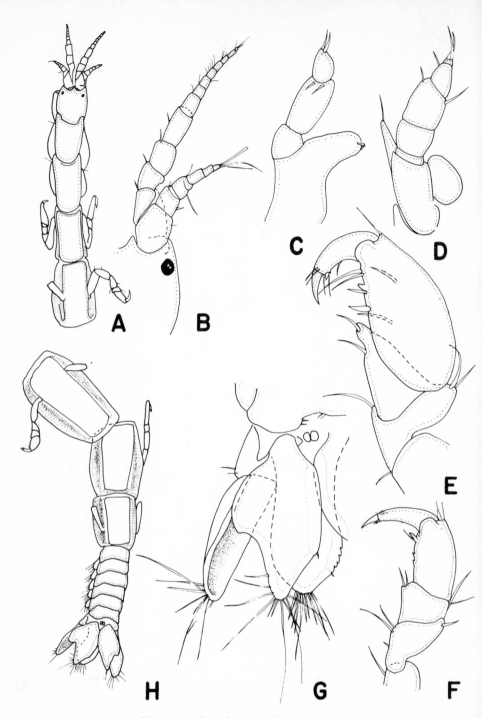

Figure 16. *Panathura formosa*, new species

A, anterior portion (approximate dimensions of entire animal: length 4.5 mm, width 0.3 mm); B, antennae; C, mandible; D, maxilliped; E, apex of first peraeopod; F, apex of seventh peraeopod; G, pleotelson and left uropods; H, posterior portion

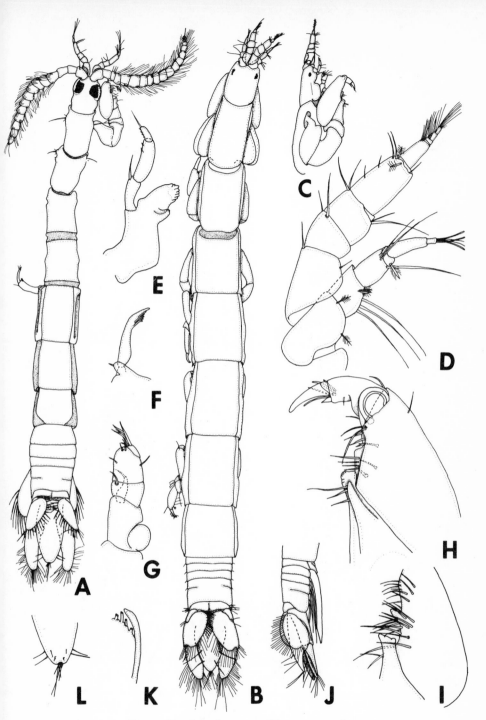

Figure 17. *Apanthura magnifica*, new species

A, whole animal, male (length 6.5 mm; width 0.5 mm); B, whole animal, female (length 8.5 mm; width 0.75 mm); C, female anterior, lateral view; D, antennae, female; E, mandible; F, first maxilla; G, maxilliped; H, apex of gnathopod, female I, carpus-propodus articulation of gnathopod, male; J, female, posterior, lateral view; K, apex of appendix masculina; L, apex of pleotelson

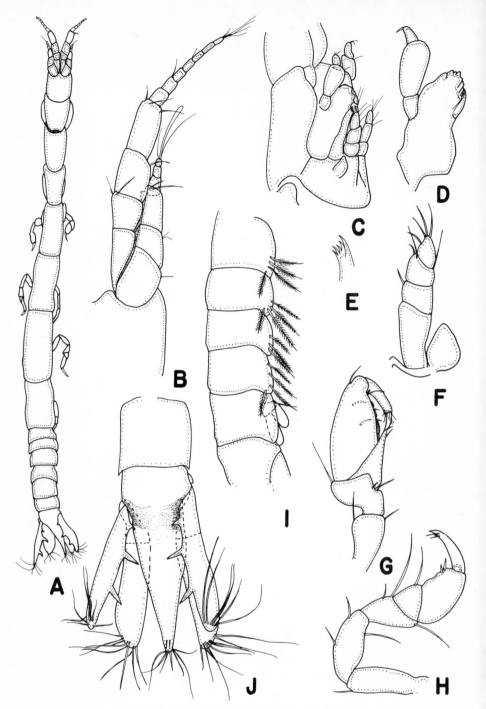

Figure 18. *Horoloanthura irpex*, new species

A, whole animal (length 3.7 mm; width 0.2 mm); B, antennae; C, cephalon, lateral view;
D, mandible; E, first maxilla; F, maxilliped; G, apex of first peraeopod; H, apex of seventh
peraeopod; I, pleon, lateral view; J, pleotelson and uropods

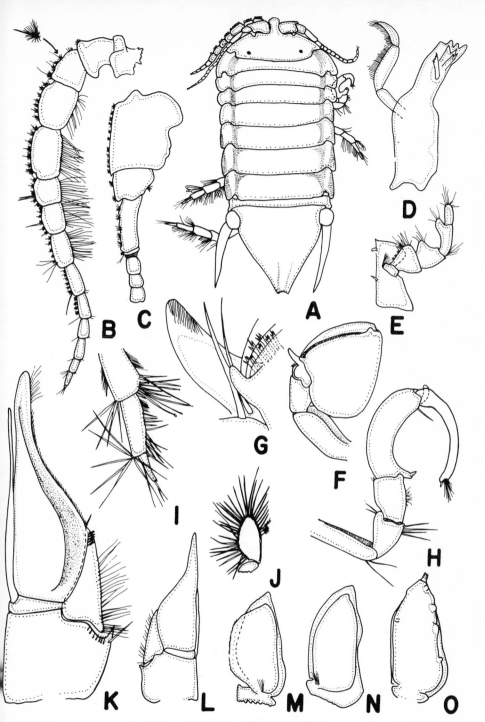

Figure 19. *Ancinus depressus* (Say)

A, whole animal, male, (length 7 mm; width 3 mm); B, first antenna; C, base of second antenna; D, mandible; E, maxilliped; F, apex of first peraeopod; G, spine at base of palm of first peraeopod; H, apex of second peraeopod; I, apex of seventh peraeopod; J, first pleopod; K, second pleopod of male, with appendix masculina; L, second pleopod; M, third pleopod; N, fourth pleopod; O, fifth pleopod

[85]

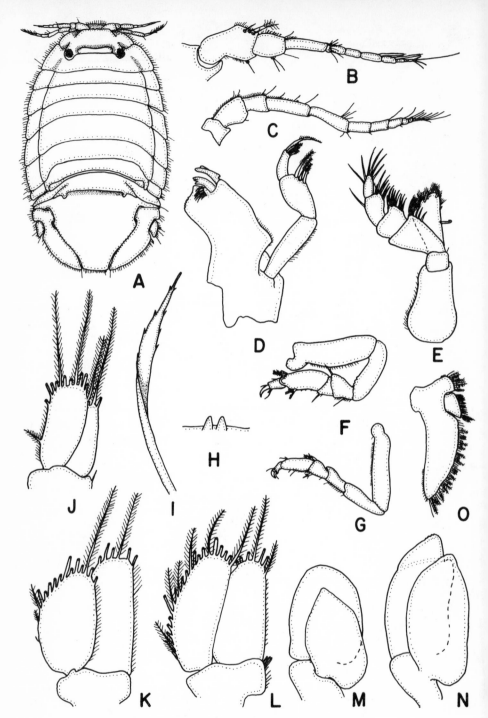

Figure 20. *Cassidinidea lunifrons* (Richardson)

A, whole female (length 4 mm; width 2.5 mm); B, first antenna; C, second antenna; D, mandible; E, maxilliped; F, first peraeopod; G, seventh peraeopod; H, penes (from male collected in Beaufort, North Carolina, length 3 mm, width 2 mm); I, apex of appendix masculina (from same male as H); J, first pleopod; K, second pleopod; L, third pleopod; M, fourth pleopod; N, fifth pleopod; O, uropod

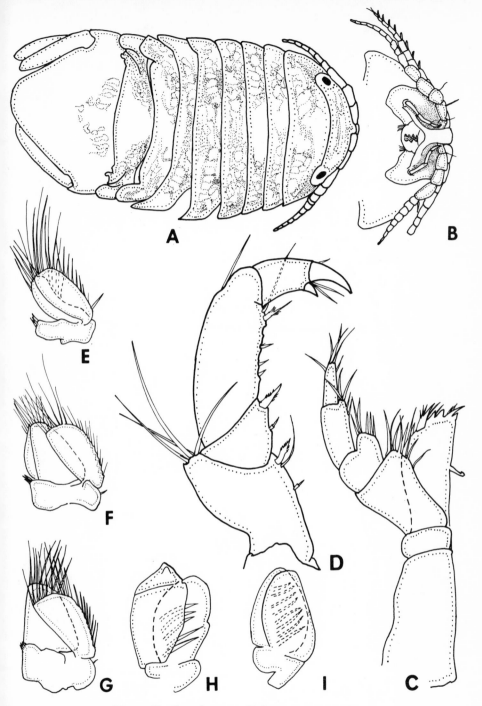

Figure 21. *Exosphaeroma diminutum*, new species

A, whole animal, male (length 2.2 mm; width 1.0 mm); B, cephalon, ventral view; C, maxilliped; D, apex of first peraeopod; E, first pleopod; F, second pleopod; G, third pleopod; H, fourth pleopod; I, fifth pleopod

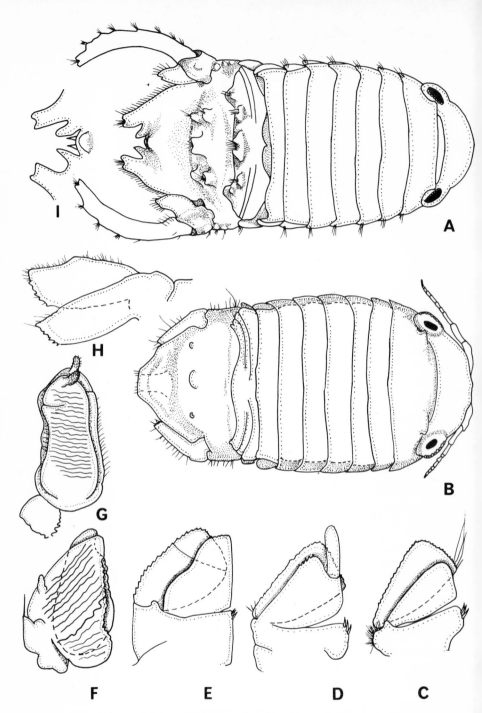

Figure 22. *Paracerceis caudata* (Say)

A, whole animal, male (length 7 mm, width 3.5 mm) ; B, whole animal, female (length 6 mm, width 3 mm) ; C, first pleopod; D, second pleopod; E, third pleopod; F, fourth pleopod; G, fifth pleopod; H, uropod; I, apex of pleotelson

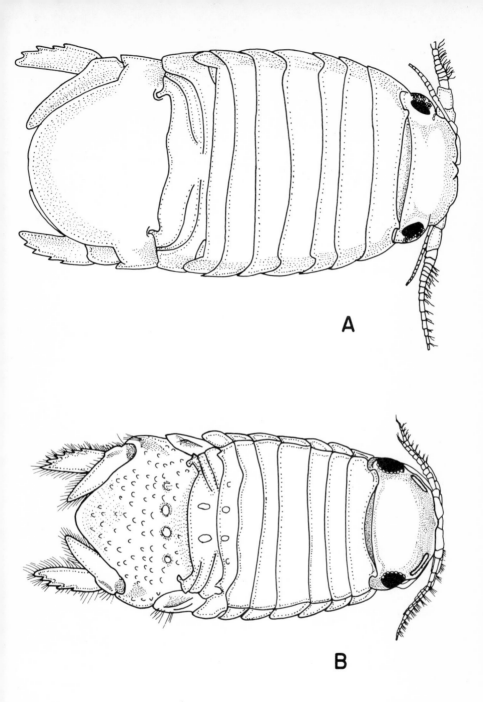

Figure 23. A, *Sphaeroma quadridentatum* (Say) ; whole animal (length 4.5 mm, width 3.5 mm) ;
B, *Sphaeroma destructor* (Richardson) ; whole animal, female, (length 10 mm; width 4 mm)

[89]

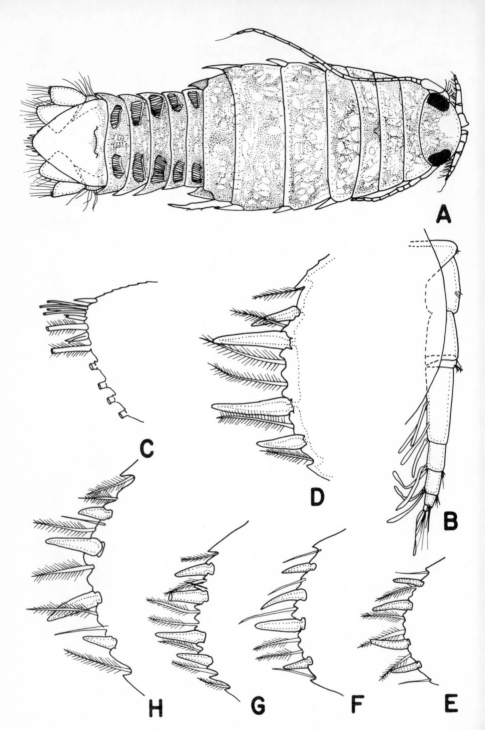

Figure 24. *Eurydice littoralis* (Moore)

A, whole animal (length 3.9; width 1.2); B, first antenna; C, apex of uropodal exopod; D, apex of pleotelson; E, apex of pleotelson from animal 1.8 mm long; F, apex of pleotelson from animal 2.4 mm long; G, apex of pleotelson from animal 2.5 mm long; H, apex of pleotelson from animal 5.0 mm long

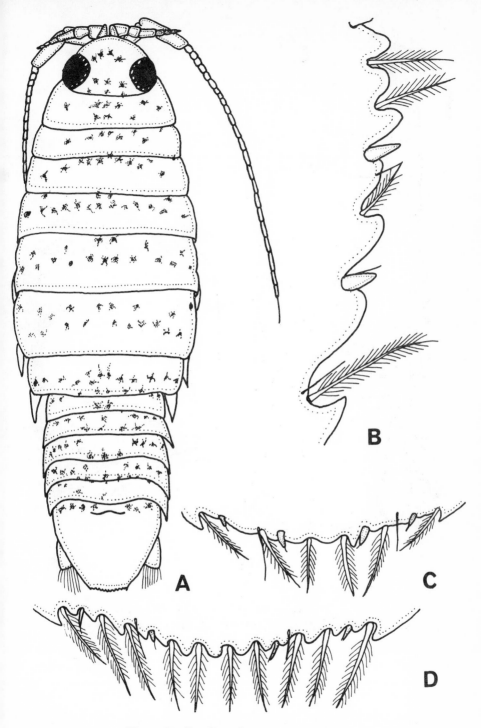

Figure 25. *Eurydice piperata*, new species

A, whole animal (length 5 mm, width 1.5 mm); B, apex of pleotelson; C, apex of pleotelson from animal 2.5 mm long; D, apex of pleotelson, left side, from animal 2.6 mm long

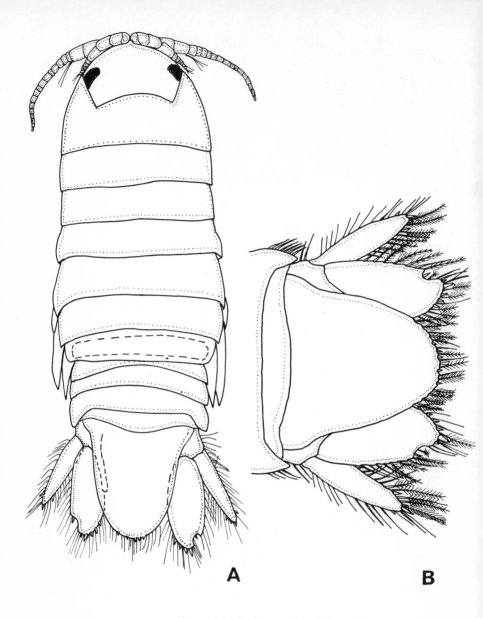

Figure 26. *Cirolana polita* (Stimpson)
A, whole animal, female (length 6 mm, width 2 mm); B, pleotelson and uropods

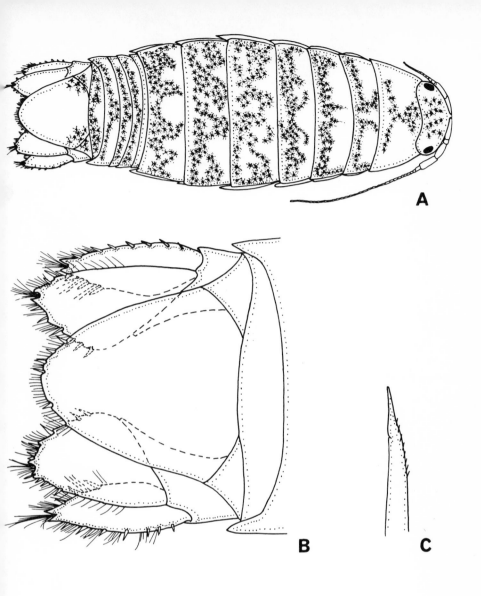

Figure 27. *Cirolana parva* (Hansen)
A, whole animal (length 9.5 mm; width 3 mm); B, pleotelson and uropods; C, apex of appendix masculina